THE LYREBIRD

THE
Lyrebird

L. H. SMITH, M.Sc., D. Phil. (Oxon)

LANSDOWNE PRESS

FIRST PUBLISHED IN 1968
BY LANSDOWNE PRESS PTY. LTD.
380 BOURKE STREET, MELBOURNE
PLANNED AND DESIGNED IN AUSTRALIA
TYPE SET BY DOVER'S PTY. LTD., MELBOURNE
PRINTED BY LEE FUNG PRINTING CO. LTD., HONG KONG

To
The Lyrebirds of Sherbrooke
who have charted
the course of my life
and but for whose patience
and trustfulness this
book would not have
been possible

CONTENTS

LIST OF ILLUSTRATIONS

COLOUR

BLACK-AND-WHITE

ACKNOWLEDGEMENTS

It is a pleasure to acknowledge the assistance of many good friends and companions of the bush in various aspects of the preparation of this book. I am especially grateful to the late Ray T. Littlejohns for having introduced me to Timothy, Sherbrooke's famous lyrebird of days gone by, and for having so readily shared his knowledge with me. I take this opportunity to say "Thank you" to the proprietors of "Sherbrooke Lodge", Mr. and Mrs. C. H. Wileman, for their warm hospitality over the years and I am greatly indebted to Mrs. Graeme McPherson, formerly Miss Dawne Wileman, for her ready co-operation in our efforts to protect the lyrebirds against the foxes and in keeping a watchful eye upon the lyrebirds in Sherbrooke Forest.

Grateful acknowledgement is also made of the encouragement given by the editors of *Wild Life*, *Walkabout*, the *National Geographic Magazine*, the *Illustrated London News*, *Sphere*, *Country Life*, etc., whose interest has taken a practical turn and enabled me to procure the photographic equipment necessary to record the behaviour of the lyrebird.

I gladly acknowledge the work of earlier "lyrebird men" whose various publications have provided valuable information to supplement and extend my own experiences. In this connexion, special mention must be made of the works of the late R. T. Littlejohns, A. H. Chisholm and various authors in the *Emu* and the *Victorian Naturalist*.

I am very much indebted to the Department of Primary Industries of Queensland, the Fauna Protection Panel of New South Wales and the Department of Fisheries and Wildlife in Victoria for their co-operation in supplying information on the legislation in the three States.

I would like to express my thanks to the Council of the State Library of Victoria for permission to use plates of Gould and Mathew (pages 1 and 14 and facing page 20), and to the Trustees of the National Museum of Victoria for permission to photograph lyrebirds' eggs (facing page 21).

I owe a special debt of gratitude to my wife, Margaret, whose unfailing help over the years alone has made it possible for me to pursue a hobby which, however fascinating, has consumed a great deal of time which might otherwise have been employed to ease the additional burden she has so cheerfully carried.

Finally, I am indebted to my publishers, Lansdowne Press, for having afforded me this opportunity of writing a further chapter in the story of the lyrebird and sharing my experiences with this wonderful bird with my readers.

L. H. SMITH
12TH NOVEMBER, 1966

FOREWORD

So much has already been written about the lyrebird and so much film has been exposed (and more frequently under-exposed!) in pursuit of photographic souvenirs of the bird, that one might well wonder whether another book on the subject could be justified. Yet the excuse for writing this book derives from this very fact, for much of the information is scattered in many places. Moreover, improvements in photographic equipment in recent years have enabled a deeper penetration of the lyrebird's secrets.

The present book does not pretend to be the last word on the lyrebird. Undoubtedly, there is much yet to be recorded, and the work of the Sherbrooke Survey Group which, since 1958, has been making a close study of the lyrebird in Sherbrooke Forest, by banding chicks in the nests and subsequently observing them in the forest, will undoubtedly add much to the present store of knowledge.

There have been persistent requests for copies of my book *The Lyrebirds of Sherbrooke*, which was published by Georgian House Pty. Ltd., Melbourne, in 1951, but which is now out of print. However, I felt it desirable to broaden the approach to the subject and this book has therefore been written in two parts.

Part I deals with the history of the discovery of the lyrebird and the subsequent study of observers from abroad and from various parts of Australia, along with some notes on lyrebirds in captivity, and on attempts to establish lyrebirds in the free state in Wilson's Promontory (Victoria) and Tasmania. A résumé of the legislation designed to protect the lyrebird in New South Wales, Queensland and Victoria, which is also included in Part I, emphasizes the need for a critical review of the laws protecting the lyrebird and for closer collaboration between the three States in this regard.

In Part II, the basic content of *The Lyrebirds of Sherbrooke* is presented, broadened as necessary by observations made during the past fifteen years in various parts of the habitat of the lyrebird in the three eastern States. In addition, an account is given of my researches on the development of the tail of the male Superb Lyrebird as he develops from a chick to a mature bird at the age of approximately eight years.

The lyrebird now seems safe in our dense hardwood forests; but, if the economy of the country should require a change in the management of these areas, the future of the lyrebird could be threatened. If these conditions should ever arise, it is to be hoped that among those on whom the decision will rest, there will be sufficient statesmanship to ensure that the habitat of the lyrebird will be adequately preserved for all time.

PART ONE

1

HISTORICAL INTRODUCTION

ALTHOUGH LYREBIRDS WERE numerous in the densely wooded gullies around Sydney Cove when the First Fleet cast anchor there on 26th January, 1788, it was not until ten years later that the first specimen of this beautiful loud-voiced bird is known to have come into the hands of the white man. Failure to discover the lyrebird earlier was no doubt due to a combination of circumstances: the early settlers were busy with occupations more directly related to their own economy and would have had no previous experience to enable them to associate the strange voice with any particular species. Even if they had heard the bird exercising its amazing powers of mimicry, they would have been little the wiser. Without first-hand knowledge of the individual bird calls so aptly reproduced by the lyrebird, the chances are remote that the human observers from the Old Country would have associated a medley of such calls with a new species of bird.

In addition, the lyrebird has remarkably acute hearing and, on hearing strange noises such as the crackling of twigs or the vibration of the earth as the intruder approaches, has a habit of silently stealing away. And although there are now many areas where lyrebirds may be approached freely, the species is essentially timid by nature and remains as elusive as ever in the greater part of its habitat.

So perhaps it is not surprising that the early settlers in Australia were a little slow in finding the remarkable bird, destined to become one of the most interesting in the world.

The circumstances of the discovery of the lyrebird comprise a story which is almost as remarkable as the lyrebird itself.

The task of maintaining order and making progress in the developing young colony was not assisted by the behaviour of the more refractory elements among the new arrivals. Sometimes prisoners escaped, and ex-convicts frequently elected to live with the natives, thereby sooner or later causing trouble for the authorities. One example may suffice to illustrate the nature of the problem confronting Governor Hunter.

A party of fourteen prisoners escaped and seized a boat. Having turned south, they abandoned seven of their number on one of the Glennie Islands off Wilson's Promontory, where they were later rescued by George Bass whilst he was returning from Westernport in the course of his epic voyage in an open whaleboat. Bass had left Sydney on 3rd December, 1797, with a crew of six stout-hearted men, in the hope of determining whether or not there was a clear passage between the island continent and Tasmania.

It is understandable therefore that Governor John Hunter, determined at last to put an end to the association of ex-convicts with the Aborigines, should have issued a decree calling on all "wild white men to surrender themselves to the police or be outlawed".

Among those who were thus restored to society was one John Wilson who, in addition to having some strange tales to relate of his life with the natives, told of having seen a large pheasant-like bird in the rugged country at the head of the Hawkesbury River.

Governor Hunter soon found a way of putting Wilson's knowledge of the bush and of the habits and language of the Aborigines to better use. On 14th January, 1798, Hunter despatched a small party, including a group of four recalcitrant Irish prisoners and four armed soldiers, along with three civilians including John Wilson and a young man named John Price. The object of the excursion was to explore the country to the south-west of Sydney. Rather fortunately, so far as the lyrebird story is concerned, the Irishmen soon became weary of the journey and had to be escorted back to Sydney. The three civilians however, led by Wilson, pushed on for the incredible distance of 100 miles or more before turning back. It was during this remarkable journey that John Price, on 26th January, 1798, shot the first lyrebird known to have been collected by a white man. Although they saw many more "pheasants" and a number of other strange creatures— emus, kangaroos and wombats — they did not obtain any more "pheasants".

Surely this was a remarkable journey; a return trip of over 300 miles, on foot, in unknown country. These pioneer explorers must have had stout hearts, as they were often without food and their clothes were in tatters when the resourceful Wilson led them back to Sydney.

Governor Hunter, well pleased to receive as a trophy the first lyrebird skin ever to reach the civilized world, shortly afterwards sent Wilson out again to obtain further specimens. Recognizing the interest these specimens would create there, Hunter sent them to three of his friends in England, one of whom was Sir Joseph Banks.

Another who knew of the discovery was Colonel David Collins, who had arrived in Sydney with Governor Phillip's First Fleet in January, 1788, and who had remained as Judge-Advocate and Colonial Secretary for the next eight years. Collins had been told the lyrebird story by Governor Hunter and, whilst in England between 1797 and 1803, had been preparing his *Account of the English Colony in New South Wales*, which appeared in two volumes in 1802.

Whilst Collins was engaged in this work, by an odd chance, another military man, Major-General Thomas Davies, made the acquaintance of the strange bird through Lady Mary Howe, to whom Governor Hunter had earlier sent a specimen of the new "Bird of Paradise". Shortly after this, Davies presented to the Linnean Society a paper on the new species of bird, which he named *Menura superba*, meaning "the superb bird with a crescent-shaped tail".

As the publication by Davies preceded that by Collins, the latter was able to use the name of "Menura superba" in his own work. Collins also referred to the amazing powers of mimicry of the lyrebird, having presumably been informed of them by Governor Hunter.

Once the lyrebird became known in Europe during the early years of the nine-

Male lyrebird singing.

teenth century, it attracted the attention of artists, to whom we must be indebted for such precious early records. Without the knowledge of the habits of the bird, artists were obliged to arrange the tail feathers to suit their own moods and, since these apparently varied considerably, we now have an interesting assortment of lyrebird paintings and drawings reposing in such famous places as the Chateau de Fontainbleu, the British Museum and the Mitchell Library, Sydney. Among the latter is a rather charming drawing executed by T. R. Browne of Newcastle, New South Wales, in 1813, which depicts the lyrebird standing with his body in full view and his tail erected in display,

the lyrate feathers being extended horizontally. What makes this drawing of extraordinary interest is that it shows the lyrebird with *sixteen* filamentary feathers in addition to the two lyrates and the two median retrices. Presumably the artist was carried away by the beauty of the bird's tail and decided to add the extra four filamentaries as a token of appreciation. At least, this is a result quite beyond the powers of any known camera!

Once on a visit to Sydney many years ago, I was taken to a quiet spot where, on an open expanse of sandstone, was a drawing of a lyrebird in flight, etched into the rock, perhaps some hundreds of years ago, by an Aborigine. He may have been the first artist to depict the lyrebird. This petroglyph is carefully guarded and was in good condition when I saw it last in 1964.

It is not the purpose of this book to trace in minute detail the history of the lyrebird; because, for one thing, this has already been done, in a most interesting manner, by A. H. Chisholm in his *Romance of the Lyrebird*. Alex Chisholm's capacity for research in this field, and in others, is well known, and his pertinacity in this regard almost prompted me to write "Detective Chisholm"!

However, it seems fair to make brief reference to the battle of the "leaders" of the day over the choice of a name for the new species. In his *Birds of Australia*, Vol. 7, Gregory Mathews lists the following:

Menura novea-hollandiae, Latham, 1801; *Menura novea-hollandiae*, Latham; *Superb menura*, Latham; *Menura superba*, Davies, Gould; *Paradisea parkinsoniana*, Shaw and Nodder, 1803; *Parkinsonius mirabilis*, Bechstein, 1811; *Menura vulgaris*, Fleming, 1822; *Menura lyrata*, Dumont, 1824; *Menura magnifica*, Lesson, 1825; *Megapodus menura*, Wagler, 1827; *Menura lyra*, Shaw, Lesson, 1831; *Menura paradisea*, Swainson, 1837; *Menura victoriae*, Gould, 1862.

Some of the names, at least, reflect the high regard the particular authorities had for the species; but, surely *Megapodus menura* takes the prize. This designation implies that the lyrebird is a mound-builder in the sense that the megapodes are, i.e., for the purpose of incubating the eggs. In fact, of course, the lyrebird's mound is used principally for display purposes, though frequently the bird will tantalize an eager observer by merely scratching the mound over to extract the food it contains, reserving his display for another occasion, when perhaps the observer is sitting, fretted with frustration, in a city office!

At all events, the species of bird which we have been considering so far is now known as *Menura superba* or the Superb Lyrebird.

Interest in the lyrebird continued unabated and, between 1838 and 1840, John Gould paid a visit to this country in order to study the bird first-hand. Gould of course was interested in other Australian birds and the result of his expedition was to increase the number of known species from 300 to 600.

Male lyrebird (Timothy), with tail spread, preparatory to display.

He spent considerable time searching for lyrebirds, especially in the Illawarra district of New South Wales. Subsequently he described his experiences in his *Handbook to the Birds of Australia* (London, 1865). With the aid of collectors Gould obtained many specimens of the Superb species, but did not actually see a male bird displaying on a mound, nor did he succeed in finding a nest occupied by a chick. One detects a note of desperation in his narrative: "Of all the birds I have ever met with, the *Menura* is by far the most shy and difficult to procure. While among the brushes, I have been surrounded by these birds, pouring forth their loud and liquid calls for days together, without being able to sight one of them and it was only by the most determined perseverance and extreme caution that I was enabled to effect this desirable object". He goes on to say that "the crackling of a stick, the rolling down of a small stone, or any other noise, however slight, is sufficient to alarm the bird, and none but those who have traversed these rugged, hot and suffocating brushes can fully understand the excessive labour attendant on the pursuit of the *Menura*. . . . . Another successful mode of procuring specimens is by wearing the tail of a fully-fledged male in the hat and keeping it constantly in motion, and concealing the person amongst the bushes, when the attention of the bird is diverted by the apparent intrusion of another of its own kind, it will be attracted within range of the gun".

Gould observed male lyrebirds chasing one another in play (see p. 88), and remarked upon the birds' curious habit of "forming numerous small round hillocks which are constantly visited during the day and upon which the male is continually trampling, at the same time erecting and spreading his tail in the most graceful manner, and uttering his various cries, sometimes pouring forth his natural notes, at others mocking those of other birds, and even the howling of the dingo".

The history of the discovery of the lyrebird and the winning of its secrets covers such a long period of time and has so many facets, that it does not seem possible here to deal with every aspect. Brief reference, however, must be made to some of the principal contributors to the lyrebird story.

Although by the middle of the nineteenth century the lyrebird was well known in Europe, the first occasion on which the egg of the Superb Lyrebird was publicly displayed was at the Melbourne Exhibition of 1854, when F. J. Williams and J. Leadbeater displayed specimens of the bird along with the egg. Sketches of the egg were sent to interested zoologists in France and Germany.

One who made interesting observations on the lyrebird was Dr. Ludwig Becker, a German scientist who had come to Australia by way of South America in 1850. Among other qualities he excelled as an artist, naturalist and geological surveyor — surely a versatile man if ever there were one! By presenting "portraits" of themselves to an Aborigine named Simon and one of his relations, Becker persuaded them to bring him the nest and egg of a "Bullan Bullan", as the natives called the Superb Lyrebird.

The nest and egg were located on 31st August (1854) and Simon delivered "the goods" to Melbourne on 4th September; but, having had to travel for five days, bearing his precious burden of the nest and egg, he had carried the egg for safe-keeping in the folds of his possum-skin jacket. He was not to know that, in fact, he was thereby carrying out the final stages of incubation, and one can imagine the delight and surprise of Dr. Becker when he had delivered into his hands the nest and egg of the Superb Lyrebird only, shortly afterwards, to see the egg break and a fully-developed embryo emerge. This was the first lyrebird ever to hatch out in captivity and one can hardly imagine two stranger foster-parents; an Aborigine of the Yarra tribe (the son of the native chief who had "sold" John Batman a large tract of land near Melbourne), and a German Doctor of Philosophy with a great red beard!

Becker was not slow to recognize the full measure of his good fortune and, with the permission of Williams and Leadbeater, made a drawing of their egg, which he sent to Professor Kaup in Germany. Kaup presented it to Professor Cabanis of Berlin for publication. Thus did the egg of our famous lyrebird become known in Europe.

Dr. Ludwig Becker later joined the ill-fated Burke and Wills expedition which left Melbourne, on 20th August, 1860, with the object of crossing the continent from south to north. He became ill with scurvy at Menindie and succumbed to the rigours of the journey at Bullo, on 29th April, 1861.

Another to make valuable and interesting contributions to the study of the lyrebird was A. J. Campbell, who gives a lively account of his experiences in his classic work *Nests and Eggs of Australian Birds*. Oddly enough, Campbell's earliest association with the lyrebird was through the activities of a member of his family who, in 1847, had persuaded a native named McNabb, of the Yarra-Yarra tribe, to obtain some tails for him. McNabb was absent for several days before returning with five tails for which he was paid one shilling each!

Mature male lyrebird (Crossed Lyrates) displaying, showing "lyre" pattern.

Nest at junction of a tall tree fern and a large fallen tree, five feet above the ground. The soft green moss on the trunk of the tree fern and the small ferns which grow upon the log exemplify the delicate beauty of the forest in its remote depths. Only an occasional shaft of sunlight penetrates into these secluded places.

Campbell sought the lyrebird in Gippsland during the 1880's and 1890's, and his narrative makes fascinating reading, even eighty years later.

On one trip he walked twenty miles between the main Gippsland Road and Neerim, in nine hours. On another excursion, he travelled alone through a vast forest, portions of which were ablaze, and he could feel the "feverish dying breath" of the trees as they crashed to earth. "The toil attending the search for the lyrebird," wrote Campbell, "is the most arduous, and must be experienced to be fully realised; because, firstly, these curious birds, contrary to the general rule, nest in winter, the wettest months of the year; consequently terribly boggy and greasy tracks have to be travelled; secondly, the physical features of the country to be scoured are of the roughest and wildest description, such as Gippsland alone can produce. You have to thread your way through closely-growing hazel scrub, knee-deep in wet ground ferns, then tear through rank rasping sword grass, cutting your very clothes, not infrequently nastily gashing your unprotected hands and face; next you may be entangled in a labyrinth of wire grass, holding you at every step and hiding treacherous logs over which your equilibrium is frequently destroyed and, landing upon your side, you grunt and struggle amongst the vegetation. To reach the opposite hill you crawl 'on all fours' over a wet saturated log which naturally bridges the gully. In accomplishing this awkward task, overhanging tree ferns laden with moisture dash in your face, drenching you nearly as much as if someone had thrown a pail of water over you. Notwithstanding the chilly weather, there is always an amount of warmth in these dark forests and gladly you halt now and again for breathing time, at the head of some lovely fern gully adorned by giant timber where you stand in one of the most picturesque silent temples of Nature."

Campbell's purpose was to locate nests, procure the eggs and collect specimens of the bird itself. His account of the difficulty of shooting the lyrebird makes interesting reading: "Although the lyrebirds were numerous, great difficulty and patience has to be exercised in procuring them, so terribly shy are they. You patrol leisurely up a gully or along a survey line until you hear a bird whistling merrily on its hillock or dancing mound, a little distance in; then you commence carefully — oh, so carefully, for one false step, one extra shuffle of the leaves, or the snapping of a twig underfoot and your prey disappears as if by magic — to crawl on your hands and knees, as often as not wriggling snake fashion on your stomach through ferns and scrub from stump to stump and from tree to tree. Listen! The bird stops singing as if instinctively knowing that danger is approaching, whereupon you have to become like a statue fixed to some fern root and dare not move a muscle; no, not even if you feel a large mosquito stinging the tip of your nose. Presently the bird commences whistling as joyously as ever. On you creep, every yard nearer so that with the excitement your heart increases in palpitation till it throbs so loudly that you fancy the bird will hear it. All the time the close humid scrub bathes you in perspiration of which great beads stand upon your forehead, then rolling off, patter on the dried leaves beneath you. Affairs are desperate now, for at last you are within shooting distance and are peering through the ferns with uplifted gun and finger trembling upon the trigger; but, alas, the bird possessing sharper eyes than you, discovers you first, and is that very second off noiselessly and unperceived".

Referring to his egg-collecting experiences, Campbell wrote, "I said I had shot ten male lyrebirds. By a strange coincidence, between the years 1884 and 1894 I either found or was present at the taking of ten nests, or an average of one egg a season, an ample reward to satisfy any working oologist". It is good to know that Campbell was satisfied!

Campbell, of course, was merely following the fashion of the day; because the Superb Lyrebird, having been introduced to the civilized world, had soon become an attraction for the sportsmen of the day, as well as scientists. The beauty of the bird's tail, which had created so much interest in England and on the Continent, proved to be the undoing of the species. The birds were hunted, dogs being used to put them up into trees from where they gazed quizzically downward at them while the sportsmen took aim. It became fashionable to display the tail feathers as a trophy in the drawing room or, if the position of the home-owner in society did not justify a drawing room, then in the kitchen, or anywhere at all, so long as the tail could be displayed. Those not so fortunate as to be able to shoot their own lyrebirds had ample opportunity to buy them from others better endowed with fire-arms or opportunities to invade the haunts of the bird. In the early days of the great slaughter, tails sold for 30/- a pair; but, as they became more plentiful, the price fell. In 1888, the year in which the colony of New South Wales issued its

Male Lyrebird (Spotty) perching — an easy mark for a "sportsman" of earlier days.

famous lyrebird stamp to mark the one hundredth year of settlement, lyrebirds' tails were freely sold in Sydney streets for 2/6 per pair.

In an informative book (1896) entitled *A Sketch of the Natural History of Australia*, G. Aflalo mentions that "two enterprising brothers recently employed a number of men to shoot the luckless birds in which, after some practice, they were unfortunately so successful that 500 dozen of the beautiful tails were reported to have reached Sydney in the course of a few weeks. It is not difficult to understand how at this rate the price of tails which, according to Bennett, was as high as 30/- a pair fifty years ago, should have fallen to one third of the price, at which figure I could have bought a hundred pairs in Sydney had I been so minded".

The lyrebird was at this time protected in two of the three eastern States, but the law was not enforced. It was not until the present century was well advanced that public opinion compelled the complete protection of the lyrebird. Did I say, "complete"? We used to think that the lyrebird was safe, but events of the last few years have been disquieting. In April, on the day before Good Friday 1963, one of Sherbrooke Forest's celebrated lyrebirds, "Spotty Junior", was killed and eaten by two runaway delinquent boys; and just before Christmas 1965, two immature lyrebirds were shot in Sherbrooke Forest, presumably "for the pot". On this occasion the culprits plucked the birds and left a number of empty shell cases behind. Despite these unhappy events, however, one has the feeling that the lyrebird species as a whole is nowadays fairly safe from human predation. Its principal enemies are feral cats and cats from houses which neighbour on their forest habitats (not only at Sherbrooke), and foxes.

While the Superb Lyrebird was thus enjoying a spate of notoriety and heading (seemingly) for extermination, its less glamorous cousin was enjoying a measure of protection in the dense forests of north-eastern New South Wales and south-eastern Queensland. It was not until 1849, nine years after the famous bird-man John Gould had visited the colony, that Frederick Strange sent a specimen of a new species of lyrebird to John Gould, in London. Bearing in mind the fate of some of those associated with the early history of the lyrebird, one feels that Gould was safer in London than in Australia. John Wilson was speared by the blacks in 1800; Strange was likewise killed in 1854 and John Gilbert, who collected for Gould, was killed by the blacks in the Gulf of Carpentaria, in June 1845.

Gould named the new species *Menura alberti*, in honour of Prince Albert, consort of Queen Victoria.

The fact that this species was discovered much later than the Superb Lyrebird and that its habitat is even more inhospitable than that of the southern species no doubt afforded a measure of protection. Loss of habitat through agricultural developments has no doubt reduced its numbers, but the species still thrives in the border country between New South Wales and Queensland. However, relatively speaking, there is a dearth of information on this species, as compared with the Superb Lyrebird, though the essential details of its economy have long been established. In general behaviour and habits it resembles the Superb Lyrebird.

currawong, the yelp of a fox terrier and the yelp of a fox. From this we learn that the fox was well established in this district nearly fifty years ago. Tregellas listed over forty different calls as being imitated by the male lyrebird.

Although he found numerous chicks in their nests and banded every one of them over a period of many years, he was puzzled as to why he never saw one of these banded birds later on.

The other great pioneer lyrebird-man was Ray T. Littlejohns who began photographing the lyrebird by movie camera in 1925 — over forty years ago! Ray Littlejohns was not only an ornithologist of high repute, but a photographer possessed of infinite patience and remarkable skill. His written works reveal a sensitive mind and a versatile pen. His concern for the well-being of the lyrebird led him to exploit every available means to stimulate public interest in this remarkable bird and he was associated, along with Tom Tregellas and M. S. R. Sharland, in the first broadcast of the lyrebird's song by the Australian Broadcasting Commission on 27th June, 1931, through 3AR and 3LO Melbourne. So popular was the broadcast that it was repeated on 5th July, 1931, when it was relayed to all States of the Commonwealth and received with perfect clarity in New South Wales and Tasmania. The lyrebird thus became the first wild bird in Australia to be brought to the public through a direct broadcast or sound film. The lyrebird's song was broadcast direct from Sherbrooke in 1932, 1933 and 1934. In all the weeks of preparation which preceded these successful performances, Ray Littlejohns played an important part in selecting the positions for the microphones. To make the broadcasts possible, it was necessary for extensions to be made to two telephone lines from half a mile away to a spot deep in the forest, one line for the transmission of the bird's song and the other for communication with the studio in Melbourne. In addition, it was necessary to construct an open-air studio within the forest, from which to control operations. The end justified the means, but what an enormous amount of work was entailed! And if the bird had not sung on the mound where it was expected to sing? Ray Littlejohns saw to that — to the delight of listeners in all States.

I am personally well able to appreciate the magnitude of the task which confronted my old friend; because, in September 1952, I was invited to assist the Australian Broadcasting Commission in making a recording for use in school broadcasts overseas. The studio staff and technicians, because of their association with school broadcasts in Melbourne, were available only during the September holidays. We set out on a fine morning; but, as we approached the forest, my heart sank. There was a high wind and the birds usually do not sing well on such days.

Our preparations were simple enough; we had merely to carry the recorder, along with microphone and lead, and a 12-volt battery, into the forest, select a suitable spot and wait for a lyrebird to sing. On any other day, almost any one of many mounds would have sufficed; but, on this day, as I made my reconnaissance, there was no sound from the birds. Finally, I selected a mound screened by sword grass, and the microphone was set in place. The group of technicians had barely had time to settle down behind a large log some forty feet away, when one of the two birds known to frequent the area appeared and went straight to the mound, where he sang for eight minutes before departing. This was the only song we heard during the entire day; but the result was pronounced excellent. I tell this story not to show "how it can be done", but to emphasize the importance of selecting the right spot for the microphone and the skill displayed in this regard by Ray Littlejohns, some twenty years earlier.

Nowadays, with the aid of portable transistorised tape recorders and sensitive microphones, it is relatively easy to record the voices of lyrebirds which have been trained, by men like Ray Littlejohns, to tolerate human intrusion; but in 1931 there were no such advantages.

Ray Littlejohns, through his writings, illustrated lectures, movie films and broadcasts, did much to popularize the lyrebird and to educate the government and the public to a better appreciation of the lyrebird and other wild creatures. He was, moreover, always willing to share his knowledge with others and perhaps the circumstances of our first meeting will bear recounting.

One Sunday morning in April 1939, my wife and I were stalking lyrebirds in a rather densely-timbered area in Sherbrooke Forest, just a little to the north-east of "The Falls". I had hopefully "attached" myself to a mature male bird and was endeavour-

Male lyrebird (Spotty), singing on a moss-covered log, shows his long tail to advantage.

ing to creep close enough to take a photograph. This was a piece of supreme optimism, because the light was very poor, but I was "sticking to my guns". Suddenly, to our dismay, we heard the sound of snapping twigs and beheld a tall man striding purposefully in our direction. The lyrebird uttered a screech and departed in haste, as I turned to greet the stranger. His manner prevented me from saying any of the things I had been thinking about his intrusion, and when he introduced himself with apologies for having disturbed "my lyrebird", I felt I was indeed in the presence of the Great. I had heard much of him — now I had met him! "You'll do better over here", he said, as he led us to the area known as "the firebreak". Thus it was that I met "Timothy", Sherbrooke's famous lyrebird of the day. Thereafter, during the next fourteen years, I spent many happy days with Timothy and Ray Littlejohns.

My meeting with Ray Littlejohns and Timothy was undoubtedly a turning point in my life, because in such company I learned the ways of the lyrebird more rapidly than would otherwise have been possible and, instead of disappointments, I began to have a little success with my photographic excursions in the forest. The chapters which follow, I hope, will convey some of the lessons I have learned and afford some indication of the joys of my companionship with lyrebirds in many places.

Female lyrebird poses seven feet from the camera.

2

LYREBIRDS IN CAPTIVITY

THE VOLUMINOUS LITERATURE on the lyrebird affords some interesting information on the behaviour of lyrebirds in captivity. One of the earliest accounts relates to a young bird which Dr. Ludwig Becker, in the 1850's, took from the nest at the age of approximately six weeks. The chick's cry of distress brought its mother which was promptly shot for a specimen. Somehow Becker kept the captive fledgeling alive for eight days — quite a remarkable feat (if one can take a dispassionate view of the matter), considering that practically nothing was then known of the feeding habits of the bird at this tender age. Dr. Becker's observations prompted him to remark that the lyrebird could easily be tamed and would do well in zoos.

A most interesting record comes from London, where A. D. Bartlett, Superintendent of the Zoological Society's Gardens, reported that on the 9th April, 1867, the Society had acquired a fine example of a lyrebird (*M. superba*). Being a young bird, its sex was unknown, but it had been "reared from the nest" and was therefore used to people.

The report does not state who the bird's foster parents were, how it was cared for while young or how it fared during the sea voyage to England, but presumably there were few if any complications. In London it was fed on a mixture of finely chopped meat mixed with bruised hempseed, earthworms, mealworms, ants' eggs, grasshoppers, together with a little canary and millet seed. One can scarce forbear to smile at the implied optimism in the inclusion of canary seed in the food mixture, but at all events the bird thrived on this essentially protein diet.

The bird quickly adapted itself to its new surroundings and created much interest by its speed of movement and ability to hop and spring "incredible distances". The bird was tame to the point of being friendly and would use its claws in a quietly persistent manner to try to force open the hand of its keeper, to obtain the food which the bird "thought" was there. In passing, I may add that I have had the same experience in the forest with an immature bird whose acquaintance I made in July 1964.

Bartlett remarked on the great strength of the bird, which could pull aside clods of earth weighing 7 lb., and on its "loud and powerful voice".

In May 1868, it was reported that a male lyrebird (*M. superba*) arrived at the zoo on April 21, "making a pair of this extraordinary bird now living in the Society's Gardens".

It is not known whether the Society received any further lyrebirds from Australia, but in the *Argus* of 28th August, 1936, A. H. Chisholm reported that "a lyrebird died in the London Zoo in 1903 and was never replaced". Inquiries have revealed that unfortunately many of the Zoological Society's records were destroyed by bombing during World War II, and the history of this bird cannot be traced. From 1867 to 1903 is a very long time and one wonders whether a lyrebird could live for more than thirty-six years. The idea should not be dismissed lightly, because the bird known as "Timothy" lived for at least twenty-five years in Sherbrooke Forest, Victoria, where he was exposed to predation from foxes and cats. The ultimate cause of his death is not known, but it could have been due to a predator. The London bird would certainly have the advantage of complete protection.

In his report of August 1936, in which he paid a tribute to "Joe" and "Zoe" for having produced the first lyrebird chick in captivity, Chisholm mentions that, in the 1880's, a settler on the Hawkesbury River succeeded in having two lyrebirds' eggs incubated by a domestic hen. In due course these birds were shipped to France; one of them (a female) died while passing through the Red Sea, but the other (a male) reached its destination and lived for over five years in a French zoological park.

Reference is made in a later chapter to two lyrebirds, "Joe" and "Zoe" which were kept in captivity in New South Wales. Because they became such famous Australian personalities it seems preferable to discuss them along with other notables, but to complete this aspect of the story, they are mentioned here.

Surely one of the most remarkable accounts of lyrebirds in captivity is that given by J. G. O'Donoghue. Referring to events which occurred towards the end of the nineteenth century, he remarked *inter alia* that, at that time, in the Crooked River district of north Gippsland, lyrebirds were "as common as sparrows and starlings in Melbourne". Another very interesting observation made by O'Donoghue was that, in 1899, the fox and rabbit were unknown in that district; in 1914 the "valley teemed with them," while the lyrebird population had dwindled to almost nothing.

Without doubt, the most remarkable portion of O'Donoghue's report deals with the interbreeding of a male lyrebird and domestic fowls claimed to have been achieved by a Victorian ornithologist, A. W. Milligan, who then lived near Traralgon in south-eastern Victoria. However, in recent years several authors have probed the literature relating to this claim and it now seems certain that Milligan's experiments began with two hybrids (a male and a female) derived from a male lyrebird and a domestic hen, the hybrids having been captured in the scrub near Traralgon and later acquired by Milligan. It was these birds which subsequently interbred. These unique birds, it is noted, when entered in a dog and poultry show in Melbourne round about 1896, were

Gregory Mathew's plate of Menura Alberti.

Witherby &

awarded a special prize. They were fowl-like in form, but built on a somewhat smaller scale. The plumage was "lax and indeterminate, and ashy brown in colour". The wing feathers, protruding in sheaths like a camel hair paint brush, closely resembled hair in texture; but in other respects, except for the voice, the birds approached more closely to the domestic hen than to the wild stock.

Milligan began a series of experiments with these hybrids, which were said to breed freely *inter se*, and had successfully reared two generations, when he broke up his home and proceeded to Western Australia.

O'Donoghue says that Milligan had reached the stage when he expected the next generation to produce the tail and other characteristics of the lyrebird. Had he done this, says O'Donoghue, he would have been the discoverer of the application of the Mendelian principles of crossing which had been announced by Gregor Mendel, an Austrian monk, in 1865.

If these remarkable claims are correct, the lyrebird, as well as Milligan, certainly missed an opportunity of achieving a place in the history of science which would have added lustre to its crown in the avian world!

Strange as it may seem that a male lyrebird should mate with a domestic hen, there is some support for Milligan's claims from other sources. A man called Davis, of Walhalla, Victoria, claimed some time prior to 1907 that "a male lyrebird mated with a black Spanish hen, which laid away in the scrub and brought out a clutch of chickens which, when they grew up, resembled a lyrebird in every way, excepting the tail of the male lyrebird".

A further report of a lyrebird-fowl hybrid relates to a claim that, some years prior to 1921, on a lonely farm near Twofold Bay in New South Wales, a fine male lyrebird had often visited the fowl-yard and that hybrids were produced which were said to be more like lyrebirds than fowls.

Lyrebird chick two-and-a-half weeks old.

Eggs of lyrebirds.

```
        5
4               6
3       9       7
2               8
        1
```

1   M. superba, *Fern Tree Gully*, 62.0 mm. x 42.0 mm.
2   M. superba, *Agnes River, Vic.*, 64.0 mm. x 41.5 mm.
3   M. superba, *Mt. Toole-be-wong, Vic.*, 61.0 mm. x 42.0 mm.
4   M. superba, *Southern Gippsland, Vic.*, 63.5 mm. x 41.5 mm.
5   M. superba, 63.5 mm. x 41.5 mm.
6   M. superba, *Clarence River District, N.S.W.*, 60.0 mm. x 41.5 mm.
7   M. superba, *Harrietville, Vic.*, 61.5 mm. x 43.0 mm.
8   M. superba, *Walcha, N.S.W.*, 61.5 mm. x 42.0 mm.
9   M. superba edwardi, *Stanthorpe District, Qld.*, 54.5 mm. x 40.0 mm.

So there it is . . . and someday no doubt an enterprising scientist will endeavour to check these claims under controlled conditions. It is to be hoped that all relevant details will be recorded for posterity, so that reliable data will replace the doubts and queries with which we are now beset.

Coming nearer home, there have been several lyrebirds kept in captivity in the Sir Colin MacKenzie Sanctuary on Badger Creek, near Healesville. Perhaps the first was one which is reported to have sought refuge from the bushfires in January, 1939. Since then however, there have been a number of females (or plaintails, anyway) which have settled down well, though attempts to establish a mature male bird in the comparatively small enclosure available prior to 1965 were not very successful.

In 1963, the Royal Automobile Club of Victoria launched an appeal among the members and raised the sum of $A31,600. To this the Government added $A13,000± and, in due course a large aviary — the largest in the world — was constructed. The aviary is 200 ft. long and 100 ft. wide, the sides being 45 ft. high. It was designed so that as much as possible of the natural vegetation could be enclosed and the environment was developed to produce the effect of a "Little Sherbrooke".

The aviary was officially opened on 15th April, 1965, by His Excellency the Governor of Victoria, Sir Rohan Delacombe. It then contained a female and a male lyrebird, the latter having been captured just a few days previously. On the day of the official opening, the male bird caused many anxious moments as he dashed himself against the wire in his endeavours to escape; but within a few days, under the persuasion of the Director of the Sanctuary, Mr. V. C. Mullett, and his staff, the bird became docile and even friendly. During the winter months of 1965 and 1966 he constructed mounds and displayed frequently, to the delight of numerous visitors to the walk-through aviary.

In both 1965 and 1966, the female built a nest and laid an egg which she brooded beyond the usual six weeks. Excitement among her human admirers was at fever heat, as the hatching of the chick was awaited; but, alas, the egg was addled on both occasions. However, my guess is that 1967 will see the first lyrebird chick hatched in the sanctuary which bred the platypus so many years ago.

In 1949, by arrangement with the Victorian State Government, two young lyrebirds were caught in the wild by Mr. David Fleay, at that time Director of the Sir Colin MacKenzie Sanctuary, and transferred to the Zoological Gardens in Adelaide, South Australia. Here they have been kept ever since in a special enclosure and, although this is perhaps not quite so large as one would like, under the watchful eyes of the zoo authorities, the birds have survived.

It was thought at the time of their capture that the birds' ages were eight months and twenty months respectively and that there was one of each sex. As events turned out, they proved to be both females and they have for many years regularly built nests and laid eggs, both of course infertile. A recent letter from the Chief Executive Officer states that one of the birds has developed the habit of eating her egg, possibly the result of a frustration drive.

In April 1966, with government approval, a mature male from Victoria was intro-

After a preening session, a male lyrebird stretches his wings and leaves his perch.

duced and appears to have settled down well, although he is reported to be rather more timid than the very well domesticated females. When I was privileged to visit the enclosure in the early 1950's the birds seemed quite unconcerned at my intrusion.

F. J. Williams, in 1881, recorded having "repeatedly counted over 40 eggs in the ovary of a female lyrebird" so that, despite the fact that the lyrebirds in question are approximately 18 and 20 years old, respectively, there are good grounds for hoping that a lyrebird chick may yet be raised in the Adelaide Zoo.

The stage seems set, then, for an interstate race to produce the first lyrebird chick. It would be ironical if the honour were to go to South Australia, because the birds there were all supplied at different times by the directors of the Sir Colin MacKenzie Sanctuary at Healesville, Victoria!

Rather surprisingly, since the lyrebird was first discovered near Sydney, the famous Taronga Zoological Park does not have a candidate in the race. The Executive Director, Sir Edward Hallstrom recently informed me that "many years ago we had one female bird, which was with us for twenty years. She never built a nest or laid an egg. At present we have two males, not yet fully matured".

3

COLONIZING EXPERIMENTS
WITH LYREBIRDS

AT ONE TIME THE lyrebird ranged widely throughout the eastern highlands extending between an area twenty-five miles east of Melbourne to the south-eastern corner of Queensland. Its range extended inland as far as Mount Buffalo and beyond — a distance of 100 miles from the coast. One of the "prize" exhibits of my early home was a tail of *Menura superba*, which must have been taken from the Locksley district in north-eastern Victoria, where my parents lived in the early years of this century.

A little over fifty years ago, Dr. E. Brooke Nicholls recorded his experiences with the lyrebird in the Bass Valley in West Gippsland, Victoria, and there is more recent evidence of their existence in the gullies lying to the north of Waratah Bay, which overlooks and extends to Wilson's Promontory. Sixty years ago they were common in the Fish Creek and Poowong districts and, no doubt, in the intervening country.

Yet, strangely, the lyrebird did not occur naturally in Wilson's Promontory which lies some twenty miles south-east of Fish Creek and, shortly after the Promontory was declared a national park, in 1909, it was thought to be an ideal place in which to establish a colony of lyrebirds. The merit of this proposal rested in the fact that, at the time, the lyrebird was considered to be anything but safe, because the bird was still hunted relentlessly, despite the fact that it had been protected by law, in Victoria, since 1887.

Certainly the numerous shady gullies, clothed as they are with the same general vegetation as the best lyrebird habitats of Gippsland, should have been ideal and, between 1910 and 1912, two male and five female lyrebirds were released in the park.

Thereafter the records of their history are meagre. They may well have survived for a time; but the numerous bushfires which swept the Promontory over the years could have destroyed any lyrebird colony which may have become established. The late Charles Barrett, well-known author and naturalist, reported in the *Herald* of 28th March, 1938, that lyrebirds were at that time well established on the Promontory and that he "had often heard them in the Lilly Pilly Gully and Sealers Cove areas". The only recent report of lyrebirds having been seen on the Promontory was made by some forestry workers who stated that they had seen three birds cross the "fire access track", during the bushfire which occurred in the northern part of the Promontory, in March – April, 1962.

More recently (January 1966), a bird was seen to cross the road and disappear into the dense gully vegetation at the foot of Mount Bishop in Wilson's Promontory

National Park. The description given suggests that the bird could have been a chick or a mature male in moult, though the possibility seems extremely remote. Nevertheless, the urge to investigate these reports is a compelling one.

The absence of lyrebirds from Wilson's Promontory no doubt has the same explanation as the fact that Tasmania likewise does not claim the species as indigenous. Seemingly, whatever the origin of the species, when its habitat on the mainland was being delineated, Wilson's Promontory and Tasmania were both islands. The formation of the land bridge now known as the Yanakie Isthmus, which joins the Promontory to the mainland, came later, but the lyrebird did not extend its habitat across the isthmus into the Promontory proper.

Because Tasmania was (and still is) free from the introduced fox, and because the lyrebird seemed to be threatened with extinction, the idea of introducing the species into Tasmania gained popular support. However, there appeared to be some doubt as to whether the bird would survive the crossing of Bass Strait in a ship and it was not until an aeroplane service had been established across the Strait in the early 1930's, that the problem of providing a safe transit appeared to have been solved. This, to say the least of it, is surprising, in view of the fact that in the 1860's lyrebirds were safely transported by sea to England and Europe.

The plan to transplant lyrebirds from the mainland to Tasmania was not lightly conceived. There was close collaboration between the appropriate government departments as well as between leading ornithologists in both States. Public support for the project was achieved through carefully planned publicity programmes. The press co-operated well, for the idea of having lyrebirds flown across Bass Strait was of considerable news value. Holyman's Airways Pty. Ltd., the pioneer air-service across Bass Strait and the forerunner of Australian National Airways, offered free transport for the lyrebirds. After the air trip, there was a journey of 138 miles by road, followed by four miles on horseback, from Hobart to Mount Field National Park, where an ideal habitat awaited the new arrivals. Arrangements were made for the road journey to be completed with all possible expedition.

The first pair of lyrebirds was caught with special spring snares by Harry Howe of Canterbury, Victoria, in the forest at the rear of Selby, not far from Sherbrooke Forest. The birds were caught "without loss of a single feather" and the photographs of the lyrebirds, along with that of the successful trapper, which appeared in the daily papers of 27th August, 1934, suggest that the birds were none the worse for their remarkable adventure and that they were certainly not concerned at the prospect of being the first lyrebirds to fly across Bass Strait and take up housekeeping in Tasmania. The male bird even gave a concert whilst held in the cage prior to the commencement of the flight.

The birds arrived safely in Tasmania on 29th August, 1934, and were duly transported to the National Park, where they were released. While the plane journey (despite the possible effects of altitude in those days before pressurization was introduced) appeared to agree with the lyrebirds, the journey on horseback was possibly not so

Female lyrebird "paused with her head on one side, looking intently in our direction".

comfortable. At all events, the male bird was found dead next day not far from where it was released. The female was reported "well".

The experiment was not abandoned. Lyrebird lovers in the Dandenongs protested, but the Royal Australian Ornithologists Union threw in its support with the protagonists of "transplantation". Ministers of the Crown and government departments rallied to the cause and the plan proceeded.

In August 1935, two male birds and a female were transported from Victoria and released in the National Park in Tasmania. All told, during August and September 1935, eight lyrebirds were released there.

On 29th August, 1938, four more lyrebirds were sent to Tasmania and further "exports" were made in succeeding years. In all, eleven pairs have been sent to Tasmania, some of them to the Hastings Caves Reserve as well as to Mount Field National Park.

Through the courtesy of Mr. A. Dunbavin Butcher, Director of Fisheries and Wildlife, Victoria, a table has been prepared, setting out the details of the releases of lyrebirds in Tasmania. The first eleven birds were caught by Harry Howe, the remainder were caught by David Fleay and a companion of the bush.

28/8/34	1 male	)	By air to National Park on 29/8/34. Tasmania reports male bird
	1 female	)	found dead on 30/8/34. Female believed well.
14/8/35	1 male		Forwarded by air and kept in a special pen. Died 22/8/35.
23/8/35	1 male		By air. Liberated in National Park.
3/9/35	1 male	)	By air 3/9/35. Liberated in National Park.
	2 females	)	
26/8/38	2 pairs		By air 26/8/38. Liberated in National Park.
5/11/41	1 male	)	By air 5/11/41. Liberated in National Park.
	2 females	)	
26/1/45	1 pair		By air. Liberated at Hastings Caves, 27/1/45.
28/5/45	2 males	)	By air. Liberated at Hastings Caves, 29/5/45.
	1 female	)	
30/5/45	1 female		By air. Liberated at Hastings Caves, 30/5/45.
30/11/49	1 female		By air. Liberated in National Park.
7/12/49	1 male		By air 8/12/49. Liberated in National Park.

Total......... 11 males, 11 females.

Reports over the years indicate that some at least of these birds have survived. Mr. Michael Sharland, who was for many years Superintendent of the Scenic Preservation Board in Tasmania and an ornithologist and photographer of high repute, organized parties to search the two areas and once found a nest with an egg in it, as well as a nest from the previous year; also a nest in the course of building. Indeed, one gully occupied by the lyrebirds within Mount Field National Park is known as "Lyrebird Gully".

Twenty years ago, that is, twelve years after the great experiment began, a Park Ranger named H. G. Cornelius reported that he had heard a lyrebird in the National Park "whistling its head off". A report just to hand (4/11/66) provides the information needed to prove that lyrebirds are indeed now established and breeding in Tasmania. In September 1966, Mr. J. B. Thwaites (Superintendent of Scenic Reserves) and Mr. Jack Green (Head Ranger, Mount Field National Park) found a nest "with a very healthy chick in it, in the Marriott Falls Scenic Reserve, which is situated two miles to the west of the National Park boundary". This is the first occasion on which a nest has been found with a live chick in it — an event of the utmost significance. Mr. Green reports having seen a number of *immature* birds, which means that breeding has been in progress for several years, as indicated by Sharland's observations.

Female lyrebird pauses on top of old stump to peer into nest, before springing on to the entrance platform to feed her chick.

A recent report from Mr. R. K. Skinner, Caves Superintendent at Hastings Caves, confirms the view that lyrebirds have also become established in that area.

There does not appear to be any likelihood that Tasmania's native birds will be endangered through the colonization within their habitat of the most accomplished songster in the world and one which, but for some odd geological mix-up, should normally have been with them without the necessity of having to be exported from the mainland. With the knowledge of what happened to the lyrebird on the mainland to guide them, we may rest assured that Tasmanians will guard well their precious lyrebirds.

Rear view of Spotty displaying.

28

4

PROTECTIVE LEGISLATION

LYREBIRDS WERE FIRST protected in New South Wales in 1879, under "The Animals Protection Act, 1879". This Act was designed to prevent the destruction of "introduced" and "native game" during their breeding seasons. Under the Act, the lyrebird was classified as "native game" and was protected during the "breeding season", i.e. 1st August to 20th February.

The Act imposed a penalty of $10.00 for possession of a lyrebird during the closed season.

Since, by 1st August, most birds would have built their nests, laid their eggs and hatched their young, it is clear that during this critical period, neither male nor female lyrebird enjoyed protection. Further, since the males would be in moult during much of the period between 1st August and 20th February, and would therefore be in less need of protection from tail hunters during this season, the practical value of this legislation is doubtful.

Recognition of the deficiencies of this legislation led to the repeal of the first Act in 1881 and to its replacement by "The Birds Protection Act 1881". The new Act was designed to encourage the importation and breeding of "introduced birds" and to prevent the destruction of certain "native game" and "song birds" during the breeding season. The taking of the eggs of these birds, including the lyrebird, was prohibited.

The new Act again listed the lyrebird as "native game", and the penalty for capturing or killing native birds or song birds during the closed season, i.e. *1st September to 29th February*, was $10.00. So far as dates are concerned, this was a retrograde step.

The penalty for having dead birds in possession was $10.00 and that for taking eggs was $1.00. What an anomaly! This suggests that, in the eyes of the law, one dead bird was equivalent to ten eggs; but since ten eggs would normally produce ten live birds, we see that one dead lyrebird equals ten live lyrebirds . . . no, you can't apply ordinary arithmetical processes here!

Spotty perched on old log.

Spotty scratching in decaying log.

The Act of 1881 was repealed in 1893 and replaced by "The Birds Protection Act 1893". This Act was intended to prevent the destruction of certain "introduced birds" and "native birds" for a five-year period and to prevent the destruction of certain "native game" birds during their breeding season. This Act differs from previous Acts in that, for the first time, the lyrebird was classified as a "native bird" and was thus given *complete* protection for a five-year period, with protection during the closed season for the succeeding years. The closed season was fixed from 1st August to 31st January.

The penalties for being in possession of a dead lyrebird and for destroying eggs remained at $10.00 and $1.00 respectively.

Two further Acts, "The Birds Protection Act 1901" and "The Birds and Animals Protection Act, 1918-1930" gave the lyrebird *complete* protection.

The latest Act, the Fauna Protection Act, 1948-1964, provides under Section 20 for protected fauna to be proclaimed "rare", and the lyrebird has been so declared. The penalty for taking or killing "rare fauna" is a maximum of $100.00 or six months imprisonment, or both.

It is likely to prove more expensive to take or kill a lyrebird in a faunal reserve or wildlife refuge, as the maximum penalty for such an offence in these areas is $200.00.

It has taken a long time to reach this goal and great credit is due to the Fauna Protection Panel in New South Wales for its persistent effort.

The Department of Primary Industries in Brisbane has been kind enough to let me have the following information regarding the legislation in Queensland.

The first direct reference to lyrebirds in Queensland legislation appears to be in "The Animals and Birds Act, 1921 - 1924" which was declared on 1st January, 1922. The penalty for taking or killing a lyrebird was fixed at $4.00 (maximum) and $2.00 (minimum).

The "Fauna Conservation Act of 1952" is more realistic; the maximum penalty currently in force is $300.00; though "the *minimum of eight dollars plus 50 cents for each of the fauna* (including the lyrebird) in respect of which the offence was committed", seems inadequate.

The protection of the lyrebird in Victoria has been a slow process of legislative evolution.

On 18th June, 1862, Victoria's first Wildlife Act (No. 161) was passed, which provided for "the Preservation of Imported Game and, during the Breeding Season, of Native Game". Strangely, the lyrebird was not listed in the schedule, i.e., it was not protected.

In 1875, however, the magpie and the lyrebird were added to the list of *native game* and protected for part of the year, i.e. 1st August to 30th November.

The penalty for killing or destroying native game was a maximum of $4.00 plus 50 cents for each bird or animal killed.

In 1887 the lyrebird, along with a number of other birds, was added to the list of *fully protected* species.

Ten years later saw the enactment of legislation enabling *sanctuaries* to be declared and it is interesting that Wilson's Promontory was the first sanctuary to be proclaimed

Silhouetted sassafras trees in Sherbrooke Gully give a suggestion of the denseness of the vegetation.

Tree ferns in Sherbrooke Gully.

in Victoria.

The penalty for killing or destroying native game out of season had by now advanced to $20.00 (maximum) plus 50 cents for each head of native game. The penalty for taking the eggs of any bird or native game was $1.00 for each egg.

A further advance was made in 1915, when the penalty for killing native birds in a sanctuary was fixed at $40.00 (maximum) plus $2.00 for each bird or animal destroyed. The Act also imposed a penalty not exceeding $40.00 for proven "wilful trespass" in a sanctuary. If the offence were committed outside a sanctuary, the penalty was a maximum of $20.00 for the first offence or not less than $10.00 or more than $100.00 for a second offence, the fee for each bird being not less than 50 cents or not more than $10.00 in all cases.

The current legislation is embodied in "An Act to Consolidate the Law Relating to the Question of Game to be Called the Game Act 1958" (No. 6828), which still provides complete protection for the lyrebird. The penalties, however, seem inadequate in terms of today's currency.

The 1958 Act prescribes a penalty for killing or destroying a lyrebird not exceeding $20.00 for the first offence and not less than $10.00 or more than $100.00 for the second or subsequent offence; in every case the penalty in respect of each bird is 50 cents (minimum) or $10.00 (maximum).

There is a penalty of $10.00 (maximum) for being in possession of native game during the closed season, or for buying, selling or consigning such a bird, along with a penalty of $10.00 for each head of native game concerned.

The latest legislation (1958) also provides a penalty of $10.00 for every person found in possession of any "flesh, feather, skin or other parts" of a lyrebird, plus a further penalty of from 50 cents to $10.00 for each such item found in possession.

Every person who wilfully takes or destroys the egg of a lyrebird is liable to a penalty of one dollar for each egg.

It is clear from this brief summary of the legislation that there is a wonderful opportunity for collaboration between the authorities of Queensland, New South Wales and Victoria with the object of making a realistic appraisal of the situation and producing some up-to-date legislation designed to protect our vanishing fauna. There is little doubt that the majority of the people would welcome such action . . . and, to be fair, it should be mentioned that the Victorian Department of Fisheries and Wildlife has the matter under close scrutiny.

*A cluster of golden-yellow fungi (*Scaly agaric *or* Pholiota squarrosa*) growing in the fork of a Silver Wattle in the depths of Sherbrooke Forest.*

Summer courtship . . . a male lyrebird singing softly to a female whilst raising his wings and spreading his tail.

PART TWO

5

EARLY EXPERIENCES IN SHERBROOKE FOREST

IT WAS MANY YEARS ago that I saw my first lyrebird. Since then I have seen many, but I shall never forget the day in August 1933, when I saw the first one in Sherbrooke Forest, some thirty miles east of Melbourne.

I knew a number of people who had seen lyrebirds in Sherbrooke and I was envious of some of my friends who had "just been walking in the forest when, suddenly, a lyrebird had run across the path". I used to marvel at their luck. I had been to Sherbrooke often and had gone off the beaten tracks looking for lyrebirds, but never a one had I seen. But I always carried my camera, just in case!

And then, one day, it really happened. I was walking down Sherbrooke Gully about half a mile below the head of "The Falls", when a dark brown form flashed across the gully and up the side of the hill. It had vanished almost before I realised it was a lyrebird.

I decided to investigate, but soon found that the going wasn't easy. There were too many obstructions; the hill was fairly steep and I was impatient with excitement. Gripping the carrying strap of my camera in my teeth, I crawled on hands and knees up the hill, into the scrub and among the musk trees.

When, all of a sudden, I saw my quarry straight ahead of me, my heart began to race. It was a female and there she was, not more than a few feet from me, scratching quietly but vigorously for worms, apparently unaware of my presence. I edged closer — ten feet, eight feet. Ah, I thought, this is the moment!

Just then she moved on a little. Cautiously I followed. I had worked hard for this photograph and the perspiration was streaming down my forehead and over my eyes, but I was not going to take the picture until I had the bird just where I wanted her. I wanted to get her directly on the side and I wasn't going to have any little twigs or bracken between me and the subject, obscuring part of her in the picture. It was going to be a perfect photograph. I was very young then.

So the chase went on for a full fifteen minutes, until at last I found myself on one end of a decaying log with the lyrebird on the other, about eight feet away. This was the moment I had waited for; with my thumb and first two fingers exultantly holding the camera release, I pressed the camera close to my body, held my breath, and . . . the lyrebird trotted off down the gully again, leaving me literally out on a limb.

I know now that neither my camera nor the film it contained was equal to the task, but I was terribly disappointed at the time. I know now that the lyrebird had been gathering worms for her chick which was hidden away in a cosy nest down in the gully, but at that time I knew nothing of nests and chicks. However, my appetite was whetted and I was determined to learn the lore of the lyrebird.

The reader would perhaps grow weary if one were to attempt to traverse in detail the tangled trails of Lyrebird Land and were to cause him to wait until Fortune favoured us with a glimpse of our quarry and until conditions were suitable for photography. But, if the reader is to be saved from this, he must forgo the pleasure of picnicking in Sherbrooke Forest, of sitting upon a log in a forest alive with the songs of birds and with the sunlight filtering down through the tall, closely packed mountain ash trees, while a lyrebird scratches energetically for food a few feet away. He must not complain if he is deprived of the joy of tramping through the forest in the early dawn, when the magic notes of the lyrebirds set one's heart racing and one's ear drums tingling; he must be denied the thrill, after a long and arduous search, of finding the nest of a lyrebird set among the ferns. Nor shall he complain if he is not to experience the joy of seeing the tall eucalypts of Sherbrooke, clothed in ghostly raiments, loom up out of the fog on a winter's day and leap into all their glory as the Sun, finally victorious, drives the mists before him into oblivion.

All these experiences, never to be forgotten, are the steps whereby one learns the lore of the lyrebird.

Sherbrooke Forest is really a three-in-one forest. At the lower level is a jungle of small trees and ferns fringing the little streams that gurgle merrily over their rocky beds; above them are the delicately scented musks and hazels, with an occasional sassafras tree, and acacias which are golden with blossom in the springtime; and towering above them all are the tall, majestic and truly wonderful mountain ash trees (*Eucalyptus regnans*).

Sherbrooke Forest consists of a number of rather steep hills and gullies, the beauty of which is not easily described. In the depths, to which the sunlight seldom penetrates, the trunks of the tall tree-ferns are bedecked with soft green moss and ferns, and fungi of many colours — orange-red, purple, yellow and white — abound. The tall straight eucalypts, many of which are over two hundred feet in height, move slowly, like giant pendulums in the gentle breeze, or sway violently in the strong winds; and frequently uproot themselves, to fall with a resounding crash smashing everything in their paths to earth. Such fallen giants provide obstacles or bridges across a gully for generations to come.

Sherbrooke is a forest of many moods — mellow in autumn; gay with song and sunshine in spring; gloomy, dull, sometimes enveloped in fog and sometimes bathed in sunshine in winter; calm and serene on a fine day; lashing angrily before the winds that come in July — but always it is alive and interesting. Sherbrooke Forest with all it contains is our common heritage, and no man may count himself poor whose treasure-house contains memories of even one day spent within its sanctuary.

Perhaps this brief glimpse of Sherbrooke will explain in some measure why it has been possible to spend over thirty years in quest of its lyrebirds, a self-imposed task by no means yet complete, in which disappointments have outnumbered successes. Com-

Base of mountain ash tree (Eucalyptus regnans).

pensation has been the joy of reposing for a brief spell upon the throbbing bosom of the forest and hearing the sweet melody of its inner voice.

6

MAINLY DESCRIPTIVE

WHILE SHERBROOKE FOREST is certainly the most widely known home of the lyrebird, it is of course not the only place where the bird is found. Its habitat extends from the Sherbrooke area through the Eastern Highlands, the Gippsland Ranges and the Australian Alps to the mountain valleys of eastern New South Wales and south-eastern Queensland. I have had some interesting experiences with the lyrebird in various parts of its range; though, because of the proximity of Sherbrooke Forest to Melbourne, most of my observations have been made on the lyrebirds of Sherbrooke.

It simply would not be possible in this book to describe every part of the lyrebird's habitat, nor would there be any point in doing so. But, although the bird is innately shy, it is frequently possible to see and hear it in unexpected places. One may enjoy the comforts of the lounge or dining room of The Chalet at Mount Buffalo National Park whilst listening to the song of the lyrebird in the nearby forest, and early-morning risers frequently see the birds scratching for food along the edges of the walking tracks.

Once I sat upon a log enjoying the song of a beautiful male lyrebird displaying on a rocky ledge within thirty yards of the railway station at the Royal National Park, near Sydney, while hundreds of visitors streamed in holiday mood out on to the walking track, quite unaware that the lyrebird was so close.

It is a great thrill in the early morning to hear the Albert Lyrebirds singing in the Lamington National Park in south-eastern Queensland, but these birds are much more difficult to see at close range than are the birds of Sherbrooke. Once, by imitating a lyrebird chick, I succeeded in enticing a female Albert Lyrebird up from a steep gully to the track where I was hiding behind a large tree; but, when the puzzled female detected my presence, she gave a loud squawk and glided down into the gully again. On another occasion, after squirming for some time through the tangled undergrowth and disentangling myself from prickly vines, I was rewarded by a momentary glimpse of an Albert Lyrebird in display, but in an instant he was off like a silver phantom, leaving me perspiring and frustrated — and hooked to a large lawyer vine. Such conditions are not conducive to close study of any bird.

I have stalked lyrebirds in many other places — in the Blue Mountains (New South Wales), in Tarra Valley and Bulga Park (Victoria) and in Mallacoota Inlet National Park (Victoria), but the birds of these regions do not welcome visitors and make prolonged observation impossible.

Tree ferns and tall eucalypts (Eucalyptus regnans) *are frequently found together in the lyrebird's habitat.*

As stated earlier, there are two species of lyrebirds, namely *Menura superba*, the Superb Lyrebird, and *Menura alberti*, the Albert Lyrebird.

The range of the Superb Lyrebird extends from eastern Victoria to south-eastern Queensland, while the Albert Lyrebird is found only in north-eastern New South Wales and south-eastern Queensland. In the "granite belt" in north-eastern New South Wales and south-eastern Queensland is found a sub-species of the Superb Lyrebird, named by A. H. Chisholm "Prince Edward's Lyrebird". Its behaviour generally is the same as that of the Superb species.

The body of the Superb Lyrebird is similar in size to that of a small domestic hen, but the feathers are not so bulky, giving the lyrebird a neater appearance. The colour is dark brown to coppery-brown above, passing through greyish to light grey between the legs and under the tail.

The tail consists of three types of feathers, numbering sixteen in all. There are two long, broad "lyrate" feathers at the sides, twelve "filamentary" feathers and two long slender "medians" in between. All these feathers are a dark brown-to-black colour on the upper side, making them difficult to distinguish against the forest floor. The two lyrate feathers are some twenty-seven to thirty (and occasionally up to thirty-six) inches long and from three to four-and-a-half inches wide. On the underside they are silvery-mauve in colour with large regular markings of golden-brown terminating in black, and the tip is black. These feathers give the impression of having "V"-shaped notches cut out of them, but this deception is due to the curious structure, which consists of a strong central quill having fine barbs on both sides. Those on the inner side are short and stiff, while those on the outer side are fine and flexible. They carry barbicels in certain portions and so mesh completely in these parts; but, where the V-notches appear, the barbicels are absent, making the feather appear from a short distance to be transparent in these parts.

The filamentary feathers, approximately thirty inches in length (longer in some birds), consist of a central quill which tapers towards the extremity and to which are attached one hundred or more fine filaments (barbs). These are up to ten inches in length, the colour being silvery-mauve on the underside and brownish-black above. The base portion of the filamentary feather consists of barbs complete with closely interlocking barbicels (that is, a fully-webbed portion) and the length of this portion of the feather varies in a regular manner with the position of the feather in the series of twelve. It is short in the side filamentaries, increasing to a maximum at the centre. Presumably this stiffening of the tail feathers is for the purpose of conferring strength.

The remaining feathers, the two slender medians, are slightly longer than the filamentaries and are silvery-white in colour on the underside, being brownish-black above. These feathers consist of a central shaft, the inner side of which is devoid (or practically so) of webbing but which carries very short widely spaced filaments (barbs); the outer side carries "webbing" which near the proximal end is extremely short but which gradually increases in length so that near the distal end it is approximately $\frac{3}{8}''$ (10 mm.) in length. The terminal two or three inches of the distal end carry widely

41

spaced filaments (barbs) ranging in length from half an inch to perhaps an inch-and-a-half. At the tip, the "shaft" is extremely thin, being comparable in thickness with the barbs themselves.

The sixteen tail feathers are "held" in a kind of flap, roughly semi-circular in shape, which is highly muscularized and capable of being raised or lowered by the bird, at will. The bases of the shafts are clearly visible from close range, when the tail is inverted. In repose, the flap is covered by the upper tail coverts.

The Albert Lyrebird differs considerably in colouring and in plumage from the southern species. The two side feathers are much shorter and lack the distinguishing V-markings, the under colouring being silvery-grey. In the early days this led to a great deal of confusion, because such pioneers as were fortunate enough to catch a glimpse of the Albert species mistook it for an immature male Superb. The filamentaries of the Albert species are finer and shorter than those of its relative. The two central retrices cross at the base, as in the case of the Superb, but are much broader and more fully webbed.

The Albert species is the more brightly coloured, the under part of the tail and throat being a bright rufous. The eyes of this species are reddish and bulbous, while those of the southern species are dark, if not black. The legs of both species are very powerful and are equipped with one rear and three front claws having large black toe-nails over one inch long, the claw-span being five-and-a-half to six inches. These very strong claws enable the bird to move large rocks and logs under which its food is found.

In several places in this book reference will be made to particular lyrebirds which

Underside of a fila-mentary feather show-ing fine structure.

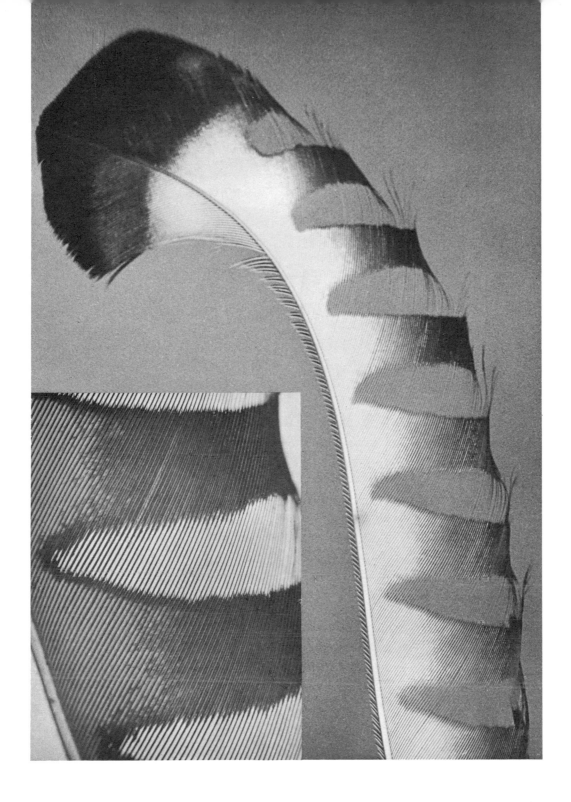

The structure of the lyrate feather and "V" markings. Inset shows detailed structure of windows in lyrate feather.

exhibited pigmentation faults in their plumage, thus rendering themselves readily identifiable. In most cases these faults are minor, but R. C. Chandler once described an "albino" lyrebird in the Bass River Valley. However, Chandler stated that the eyes were black, so that the bird was not really an albino.

The lyrebird is by nature an extremely shy creature. It dwells principally in the deep fern gullies and on the sides of the hills which flank them. In such country it is extremely difficult for a person to walk without making considerable noise, because of the denseness of the undergrowth and the fact that the forest floor is strewn with fallen trees and branches, leaves and twigs. Only those who have tried to stalk lyrebirds in such country can fully appreciate the difficulties and the extreme exertion which is required. Usually, after a period of intense concentration and cat-walking, you find at the last fateful moment, when you might reasonably have hoped to catch a glimpse of your quarry, that the alluring singing has stopped and that the bird has vanished.

It is only in Sherbrooke Forest that the birds can be seen and studied with any freedom — which explains why so many visitors to Australia have been taken to that charming spot.

The lyrebird is somewhat curious and that, perhaps, is the reason why, over a period of years, as civilization has encroached upon the domain of the bird in Sherbrooke, it has developed a surprising tolerance towards human intruders. Because of this, it has been possible for me, over a span of three decades, to win the confidence of many of these birds and to find them regularly. In some cases I feel sure, too, that the birds have learned to recognize me and come when I call them. I am inclined to think that the birds recognize me, partly at least, by the old and neutral-coloured clothes I wear in the forest. Mrs. McPherson, who before her marriage spent much time in the forest, has often remarked that, when she failed to wear a certain blue jacket to which the birds had become accustomed, her reception was much less spontaneous.

Numerous instances could be given to illustrate the curiosity of the lyrebird. On one occasion, in the dusk of a January evening, my wife and I were on the point of leaving the forest when we heard a lyrebird call from the gully. We crept quietly to a spot which we judged to be near that whence the call had come and screened ourselves behind a large tree-fern. After a short while a female lyrebird came slowly up the gully, obviously suspecting our presence and paused, with head on one side, looking intently in our direction. As we remained motionless, she came cautiously forward, paused for a long while about three feet away and then poked her head round the tree-fern to examine the two human statues. As they gave her no special cause for alarm, she sprang into the tree-fern and began to chortle, obviously puzzled, but by no means alarmed. Eventually, with a final look at us, she left the area.

On another occasion, in the hope of obtaining a photograph of an immature male, I secreted myself behind a clump of trees with my body pressed close to the earth and remained motionless for quite some time. My pulse quickened somewhat when I saw a fine young male leave the side of the hill and approach a mound on which I had hoped he would display. Instead, after a desultory scratch or two on the mound, he stalked over and poked his head into my "hide", gazing intently at me for about a minute before quietly turning away. A minute is a very long time to do without breath and hold one's eyelids motionless whilst being closely scrutinized by a lyrebird!

I have had similar experiences with female lyrebirds, which have stood four or five feet away intently regarding the strange form they have so unexpectedly encountered in their feeding grounds.

Lyrebird's mound in a secluded part of the forest.

7
THE MALE LYREBIRD

THE LYREBIRD'S YEAR is divided into well-defined periods.

Throughout the summer the birds are on vacation, so far as domestic duties are concerned, and spend most of the day combing the forest floor for food. This consists of worms, grubs, centipedes and an occasional scorpion, found in the ground or under small logs or rocks which are frequently pulled aside to expose the soft damp patch beneath. Occasionally, an unhappy land crab falls victim to the remarkably sharp eyes of the lyrebird; and particular favourites, small indeed but obviously tasty, are the tiny shrimp-like crustaceans which abound in the moist earth. When uncovered they hop, thereby rendering themselves more readily detectable and, if the lyrebird should happen to miss them, they are taken by the little yellow-breasted robin which is the almost constant companion of the large bird.

Spotty finds a large worm and regards it with a cautious eye.

Spotty folds the worm and prepares to eat it.

Brrrpp! . . . Spotty has indigestion!

Male bird breaking down bracken fern to prepare a mound.

During the summer months, apart from early morning and later in the evening, the birds are fairly quiet, but in the autumn there comes a change in the tempo of Lyrebird Land. Because of the long period of incubation and the nest life of the chick, the lyrebird mates in early winter and, as a prelude to mating, which normally occurs in June, the male birds begin to sing and display for the purpose of stimulating themselves and their mates.

This is a period of excitement and tremendous emotional activity for the birds. From early dawn, the forest resounds with the song of the males, which even pause in their quest for food to release a burst of melody. Then, too, the mounds have to be prepared, because the lyrebird does not merely sing — he requires a special stage on which to display his passion and woo the object of his devotion.

Each male constructs, amidst the ferns or bracken, a number of mounds by clearing away all shrubs, ferns and bracken, etc., so that a circular space some four or five feet in diameter is available. The earth is scratched up into a mound which is several inches higher in the centre than at the edges. In clearing this space the bird shows remarkable ingenuity. Frequently the mound will be in the heart of a dense patch of bracken and, in order to get a start, the bird jumps upon the bracken until it has been flattened sufficiently for him to remove a stalk from the ground. This he does by digging at the roots and by clutching the stem in one claw and working it back and forth until it snaps. Other stalks are then removed in a similar manner until a sufficient area has been cleared.

Each mature male bird keeps more or less to his own territory, which may have a radius of two hundred yards, but there is a certain amount of over-lapping. Within this area each bird may have as many as a dozen display mounds, which are used from time to time, although there are usually certain mounds more favoured than others. Some mounds are used for only one season, possibly being neglected after a few weeks or months, while others may be refurbished at the commencement of the following season and serve for two or three years. In certain parts of Sherbrooke there are mounds which have been in use by successive lyrebird owners for over twenty-five years. Some of these mounds are more or less the personal property of one particular bird throughout his life, while others have served a number of lyrebirds, both mature and immature.

The antics of a pair of lyrebirds during the courting period are fascinating to observe. At times, when the female pays homage to her mate upon the mound, or runs to her lord when they meet in the forest, she appears an affectionate creature — and so she is. But she can also be coy. In the early days of May, before the actual mating has occurred, she may be observed strolling through the forest while her attendant male sings softly to her, following her with his tail partly unfolded and wings raised. She gives the impression of being uninterested and may even scratch for food while her swain pleads his allegiance.

At other times he is more ardent and less patient. A disturbance in the ferns may on investigation prove to be due to two lyrebirds in hot pursuit the one of the other, with the female leading. Their wild course takes them up the side of the hill the while they make peculiar grunting noises. The tiring female now introduces a new ruse by spring-

49

ing on to a low limb, then rising higher and higher, pursued by the resolute male. Eventually the female reaches a height of one hundred feet or more above the ground and runs out along the limb of a tall tree with the male rapidly gaining ground, and then she smartly glides to earth and disappears among the undergrowth. Her baffled mate, after pausing momentarily on his lofty perch, glides downward to continue his love-making and within a few minutes the two birds may be heard thudding up the hillside again in a repetition of the performance.

During the breeding season, from May to September, the male lyrebird may display several times in the day. There is usually a period of preparation before the actual display. The bird may be seen to be restless, unable to concentrate upon his feeding, pausing frequently and singing. When the intensity of his song suddenly increases, it becomes clear that a display is imminent. Immediately, the bird begins to run — not just a trot, but a special kind of run — which is a clear indication that he is heading for a mound. There is in his eye, indeed in his whole bearing, a look of determination and nothing short of direct intervention can stop him.

His long powerful legs carry him swiftly to his mound. Here he pauses for a short spell to inspect the stage. He scratches up the rich chocolate soil; perhaps he gives a short burst of melody. He may stay or he may depart and settle down upon another mound a short distance away.

Suddenly there arises a whirring snapping sound — it is the prelude to the display. In another instant the bird's long tail is thrown forward over his head, concealing his body beneath a canopy of shimmering silvery filaments. The sight is breath-taking; the transformation from the plain brownish-black bird to this spectacle of swaying thread-like plumage is almost incredible. You see no body; you merely hear a voice clothed, as it were, in a silver raiment. And what wondrous melody pours forth from the depths of the bird's being! Did Pan come into the forest, then he too must lie down and listen.

The early part of the song (which follows the whirring snapping sound as of scissors being sharpened) is a powerful note, a note of challenge. But the lyrebird is a master of mimicry and soon, in rapid succession, the listener hears the calls of many birds of the forest, all rendered with a precision which has earned for the lyrebird the title "Prince of Mocking Birds".

Menura's repertoire is wide and varied; he imitates the loud raucous screeching of the black cockatoo, the sharp ringing call of the whip-bird and the soft reply of the female to her mate, the hearty laughter of the kookaburra, the gurgling notes of the young kookaburra, the rather harsh notes of the currawong, the fluty notes of the butcher bird, the liquid notes of the melodious grey thrush, the twittering of the English blackbird (an introduced species), the soft piping of the yellow-breasted robin, the

ABOVE RIGHT: *Female lyrebird has gone under Spotty's outspread tail during the mating season. The bird whose body can be seen is the female.*

BELOW RIGHT: *Side view showing the female under Spotty's tail.*

carolling of the magpie, the excited chattering of the little grey fantail, the melodious notes of the pilot bird, the calls of the various honeyeaters, the subdued notes of the small scrub wrens, the notes of the mountain rosellas and, most remarkable of all perhaps, the rustling of the wings of a flock of rosellas or of a magpie in flight. From one call to another without pause, for minutes on end and, interspersed with the performer's own challenging call and other special lyrebird notes, the song may continue for half an hour or longer. During this period the bird may pause momentarily to change his position on the mound or to scratch up the earth again with long raking strokes, but essentially the display is continuous.

Sometimes while the bird is on the mound, the female will honour him with a brief visit and, as she approaches, his excitement (shared by the observer) is intensified. His tail feathers are caused to vibrate rapidly and his body sways rhythmically from side to side and, when his mate comes on to the mound, he endeavours to cover her with his silvery parasol, as they circle one another in their ecstasy. Usually the female does not stay long, merely to express her affection for her mate by touching her beak to his. Sometimes the male bird will follow her into the forest, but usually he will remain on the mound to continue his display with increased fervour.

During the display the position of the tail may change many times; sometimes the body will be completely obscured, at other times the tail may be raised with the feathers more closely grouped as in the traditional lyre pattern. It is a thrill to watch the bird manipulate his long feathers over which he has perfect control at all times.

Frequently towards the end of a display the bird stands still, meanwhile twittering the soft notes of the scrub wrens, for several minutes. Suddenly, the tail is lowered into its normal position and the feathers are shaken to settle them into place; next the artist raises his crest or topknot, as if bidding farewell to the object of his devotions, before walking sedately off the mound into the forest. The display is over.

The performance may be repeated later in the day, several times perhaps, depending upon the time of the year, the weather and the mood of the bird.

The weather has a profound effect on the display behaviour of the lyrebird. On windy days displays are at a minimum. In light misty rain, the lyrebirds sing and display well, but they do not relish the rain itself and will frequently take shelter under the dead fronds which are still attached to a tree-fern.

Sometimes in Sherbrooke Forest, in September, there will be very low temperatures, accompanied by hail or snow. The birds sing well in the cold weather, but object to being pelted with hail. Once (September 1947) I was "all set" to photograph Timothy on a beautiful mound when, suddenly, hail began to fall. Timothy stood his ground for a minute or so, while the hail bounced off his back, but finally, with a gesture of annoy-

Spotty displaying.

A close-up of Spotty singing and displaying.

ance(?), he stalked off the mound. On another occasion, he was displaying well, when the sun emerged from behind a cloud and caught his eye. He shook his head, just as a human being might well do under similar circumstances, and ceased displaying immediately.

Once (September 1942), when the ground was covered with snow for three days, Timothy did not display on his mounds during this period; but, on the third day, he strode on to one of his favourite mounds, scratched the snow away and displayed and sang beautifully. He simply could not restrain himself any longer!

Occasionally the bird performs what, for want of a better name, has come to be known as "the dance". Whilst still singing and displaying, he takes regular steps forward, sideways and backwards, with the body swaying rhythmically from side to side, and then, to the accompaniment of a special "clonk clonk" call, he jumps from one foot to the other. It is an amazing spectacle, bearing a marked resemblance to the ceremonial

Son of Spotty displaying.

Crossed Lyrates — shimmering.

Rear view of male lyrebird with tail erected during display.

dance of a native tribe.

    The song of the lyrebird varies a great deal in both content and quality throughout the range of the species. At the risk of precipitating an interstate controversy, I venture to suggest that the lyrebirds of Sherbrooke have more rounded tones than those of the Royal National Park near Sydney (N.S.W.). These latter birds have rather metallic notes. The notes of the Albert species in southern Queensland are likewise more metallic than those of the southern Victorian bird. The lyrebirds of Bulga Park* and Tarra Valley* resemble generally the birds of Sherbrooke, so far as their song is concerned, though detailed analysis may reveal differences. But it must be remembered that individual birds within one particular area such as Sherbrooke exhibit quite striking differences in their song characteristics whilst still having the same general type of song pattern.

*These are areas of mountain ash forests, similar to Sherbrooke, in south Gippsland, Victoria.

Certain birds have the habit of introducing a distinct ripple into their loud ringing notes; the effect is delightful but impossible to describe, though once heard is never forgotten. Moreover, the song characteristics of the male parent appear to be inherited by the offspring; at all events there are now several near-mature and mature males in Sherbrooke whose song characteristics are strikingly similar to those of "Spotty", the bird which dominated a particular area for some fourteen years and died in March 1964. The song of the lyrebird has been the subject of a number of very interesting and important papers by K. C. Halafoff, who has devoted considerable time and remarkable ingenuity to this study.

It seems only fitting to mention that the lyrebird is not alone in this; other species such as the whipbird and the grey thrush exhibit differences in song characteristics in different areas. Nor is the lyrebird the only species within its own habitat with a capacity for mimicry; one of the most delightful bird songs I have ever heard was from a grey

Two lyrebirds in a favourite bathing pool in a secluded gully in Sherbrooke Forest.

thrush, in Bulga Park, imitating a lyrebird! In October 1966, I was intrigued to hear a grey thrush doing likewise in Sherbrooke. This bird had worked the call of the whip-bird into its own sweet melody.

The repertoire of the lyrebird is not limited to bird calls and there are some remarkable stories concerning his wonderful powers of mimicry. There is the tale of a hungry swagman who was drawn off the track to seek the company (and food) of the bushman whose saw he could hear so distinctly in the gully below. After clambering laboriously down the steep slope for some time, he realised his mistake and the lyrebird, hearing him approaching, ceased his singing.

The lyrebird seems to have a special liking for the barking of a dog. A team of men employed in making tracks in Sherbrooke many years ago had a fox terrier in the camp and the lyrebirds nearby soon learned to imitate the barking of the dog. It would appear, too, that the call has been passed on from the adult birds to the young ones. I remember in March 1939, several years after the dog had left, watching a female accompanied by one of her offspring in this area, and was interested to hear the female giving a very good imitation of the fox terrier. When she ceased, the younger bird began to "bark" and seemed very pleased with his efforts.

Recently I was amused and at the same time dismayed to hear one of my favourite lyrebirds imitating the barking of a very large dog, complete with the panting caused by the dog's exertions. Here was certain proof that a dog had been trespassing in the forest!

Male lyrebird preening after a bath. He was running one of his lyrate feathers through his beak when photographed.

Spotty stretching a wing whilst preening.

The imitated calls rendered by the lyrebird will naturally depend on the experiences of the particular bird. In a very interesting account of "A Trip to the Bass Valley" in 1911, Dr. E. Brooke Nicholls mentioned that one bird imitated no fewer than twenty-seven different sounds. Many of these were similar to those mentioned previously, but some special ones included the koala (!), a young magpie being fed, the starling (an introduced bird), the satin bower-bird, the whistling eagle, and the "choo choo choo" noise of a steam train (heard in a valley four-and-a-half miles away).

I once heard a lyrebird giving a perfect imitation of a water ram, in the rugged country to the north of Mallacoota Inlet in far-eastern Victoria.

When not displaying or singing, the lyrebird spends most of his time combing the forest floor with his large rake-like claws in search of food and often has occasion to shift rather large logs, perhaps three or four inches thick. It comes as a surprise to see this elegant-looking bird seize a log in his claws and thrust it aside as if it were a twig.

Several times each day the male lyrebird preens his feathers most meticulously, sometimes for a period of ten minutes or longer. Each bird has a number of preferred perches from which the moss or bark has been worn away through long use. At the conclusion of his toilet, the bird raises his wings, stretches himself and either springs or glides to earth to resume feeding.

Lyrebirds — male, female and immature — love to bathe in a secluded pool in the

Spotty scratching his eye . . . a delicate operation.

gully. The entire body is immersed and the head is ducked under also. The bird may spend five to ten minutes splashing in the water, following which it shakes itself vigorously to remove the excess water from the feathers. The bird shows remarkable ingenuity when it draws the tail feathers through its beak to squeeze the water out and, as each feather in turn is released, it springs back into position behind the body, sometimes showering the eager observer with fine spray. It is too much to imagine that the bird understands the mechanics of this preliminary drying process, but the technique could hardly be improved upon. After this, the bird springs on to a favourite perch where it preens for a further quarter of an hour or so. This phase of the drying operation consists of manipulating the feathers of the entire body with the beak so as to expose the surface to the atmosphere, thus promoting evaporation of the excess moisture.

At the end of the season, from September onwards, the mature male birds begin to moult and, over a period of one-and-a-half to four weeks, shed all sixteen tail feathers. Without their beautiful adornments they present a rather forlorn appearance, but this does not prevent them from singing just as beautifully as ever, nor is the urge to display yet quite dead. Sometimes a bird will stand upon a mound and go through the motions of a display, to the accompaniment of his own beautiful song, with the little tuft of a tail dancing joyously. So far I have failed to photograph the bird whilst thus engaged.

Spotty in moult showing the new tail beginning to grow. Note the fine detail of the first filamentary feather and the dark tip of the lyrate.

A close-up (from thirty inches) showing how the tail feathers grow out of the sheaths full of pulp. The white spots on the shafts indicate emerging filaments (barbs).

The new tail takes approximately twelve weeks to grow. During this time, the male lyrebird spends much of his time in the company of others of his kind and one may frequently find a group of four or five "bobtails" in company with half a dozen "plain-tails" (females and immature males).

By the end of December the new tail will have been restored to its full beauty and the bird sings and displays again, though perhaps with less fervour than in the autumn.

During the late summer, the birds undergo a "head and neck" moult. By the end of February, with their heads and necks bare to the skin, the birds look positively grotesque; nevertheless, they frequently sing and display with great enthusiasm. By April, their heads and necks are sleek again.

The summer courtship of any interested plaintail by a mature male lyrebird is a joy to behold. I recall how, on New Year's Day 1958, Spotty followed a plaintail through the forest, singing and displaying, raising his wings and doing all those things which an ardent swain would do to proclaim his love. He was under very heavy pressure from three other males which approached from different directions as Spotty courted his "female". When they approached too close, Spotty, unable to stand the strain any longer, would leave his female and charge the enemy, putting them to rout down the hillside, to the accompaniment of loud squawks and alarm calls. Within a few minutes he could be heard thudding up the slope again to resume his love-making.

It is quite possible that the plaintail was in fact a young male, not a female at all, because it is virtually impossible to distinguish between the two, but this does not worry an amorous male lyrebird when he is in the mood.

What makes this so interesting is the fact that Spotty's own mate of 1957 was busy tending her five-months-old chick and unable to share in her mate's love-offering.

Nor was this the only evidence of Spotty's philandering. In June 1960, during the mating period, I once saw him displaying on a mound, attended by two well-known females, "Droopy" and "The Landslide Female". He was such a charmer!

To be fair to Spotty, it should be mentioned that "The Wanderer" has been observed courting two different females at the extreme ends of his territory and it seems likely, from the disposition of their mounds, that mature male lyrebirds mate with several different females which occupy areas of the forest adjoining fairly widely separated groups of mounds within the larger territory belonging to a particular male bird.

Considering that the lyrebird is essentially a ground dweller and a very poor flier, it is perhaps surprising that he generally roosts at a considerable height above the ground. At the end of the day, he may be seen springing from limb to limb, zigzagwise, as he goes higher and higher towards the crown of a tall mountain ash or a blackwood tree to

Crossed Lyrates — full face display.

Spotty in moult and growing a new tail, scratching the top of his head during a preening session.

his roosting perch, at the end of a slender branch. From this elevation he often gives a soft melodious warble before completing his preening and settling down for the night. No doubt his choice of perch is dictated by fear of forest prowlers. During the summer, especially on a moonlight night, the birds may frequently be heard warbling from their roosting perches. It is here that they "record" the night call of the spur-winged plover in flight; later they surprise their human admirers by faithfully reproducing the song of a bird which at no time dwells within the lyrebird's forest. It is during their sleepless hours also that they learn the guttural notes of the possum and the call of the boobook owl.

Spotty taking a drink from a knot-hole in a limb of a fallen tree.

Spotty in pool.

Spotty courting plaintail on New Year's Day, 1958.

From his lofty platform the lyrebird greets the dawn with song, which may continue for a quarter of an hour before he descends in a glorious glide to his feeding ground. Standing beneath the gay troubadour, admiring his artistry and fairly absorbing the atmosphere, one readily forgets the chill of a winter's morning.

BIRDS WHOSE CALLS ARE IMITATED BY THE LYREBIRD

Common Name	Scientific Name
Australian Ground Thrush	*Oreocincla lunulata*
Black Cockatoo	*Calyptorhyncus funereus*
Blackbird — an introduced species	*Turdus merula* Linnaeus
Boobook Owl	*Ninox boobook*
Brown-headed Honeyeater	*Melithreptus brevirostris* Vigors and Horsfield

Butcher Bird	*Cracticus torquatus*
Crimson Rosella (Mountain Rosella, Red Lory)	*Platycercus elegans* Gmelin
Crescent Honeyeater	*Phylidonyris pyrrhoptera* Latham
Currawong	*Strepera melanoptera* Gould
Eastern Shrike Tit	*Falcunculus frontatis* Latham
Fantail Cuckoo	*Cacomantis pyrrhophanus* Latham
Gang-gang Cockatoo	*Callocephalon fimbriatum*
Grey Fantail	*Rhipidura fuliginosa* Gmelin
Grey Thrush	*Colluricincla harmonica* Latham
Golden Whistler	*Pachycephala pectoralis* Latham
Goshawk	*Astur fasciatus*
Kookaburra	*Dacelo gigas* Boddaert
Magpie	*Gymnorhina hypoleuca* Gould
Pilot Bird	*Pycnoptilus floccosus* Gould
Scrub Wren	*Sericornis frontalis* Vigors and Horsfield
Spur-winged Plover	*Lobibyx novae hollandiae* Stephens
Thornbill	*Acanthiza pusilla* Shaw
Whip Bird	*Psophodes olivaceus* Latham
White-throated Tree Creeper	*Climacterus leucophaea* Latham
Yellow-breasted Robin	*Eopsaltria australis* Shaw

8

THE FEMALE LYREBIRD — LADY OF ALL WORK

THE MALE LYREBIRD takes no part in the building of the nest, the brooding of the egg or the rearing of the young one. These duties he leaves entirely to his mate.

The "lady of all work" is generally similar in colouring to the male, but lacks his spectacular tail. Her tail consists of fourteen plain broad feathers, the two medians being longer and more tapered than the other twelve; in addition there are two side or lyrate feathers which, however, lack the well-defined black tips characterizing the mature male, and the "windows" or V-markings are likewise less clearly defined than those in the lyrates of the mature male. Generally, the tail of the female resembles that of an immature male in his third or fourth year.

Years of observation have brought the conviction that the female is a distinctly sagacious creature. For one thing, she builds her nest in the autumn when the heavy dews make the sticks more pliable.

The nest consists of two portions; first, an outer nest of sticks varying in thickness from a sixteenth of an inch to half an inch, which are laced very tightly together; second, an inner nest constructed of fine material, principally the roots of tree-ferns. The result is a structure some twenty-four to thirty inches from front to back, a similar distance from top to bottom and eighteen inches wide. The wall is about three inches thick. The entrance is at the side and the cavity is domed to accommodate the large bird which is some thirty inches in length. Inside, the nest is about twelve inches wide, thirteen to fourteen inches from front to back and approximately twelve inches from top to bottom. The opening at the front is seven to eight inches across and roughly circular. The bottom of the cavity slopes downward to the rear, to ensure that the egg will not roll out, and it is enlarged at the top in order to accommodate the bird's tail as she sits in the nest. This enlargement of the cavity serves a useful purpose later on when the growing chick requires to exercise himself, which he does by standing up and stretching to his full height.

Lyrebirds select their nest sites with rare taste and discretion. It is difficult to say what is the favourite type of site, although that between two trees or on top of an old stump is a very popular one. The cardinal points are convenience and accessibility for the bird, together with camouflage potentialities. Nests are frequently built overlooking a small stream, even at ground level, or at the junction of two tree-ferns, and are decorated with bark or overgrown with wiregrass. Sometimes they are built in the forks of

Female lyrebird showing rounded wings and light underside of tail feathers.

Female lyrebird carrying nesting material to nest on top of tall tree fern.

large trees. Once I found a nest built in a cavity in the bank of a creek, amongst the roots of a large tree which had been exposed by erosion. The bird had evidently considered that the nest would be sufficiently protected from the weather by the earth, because she had dispensed with the outer nest of sticks.

In some parts of Gippsland (e.g., the Mitchell River Gorges) and in the sandstone country of New South Wales (e.g., Royal National Park and Hawkesbury River Gorges), the lyrebird places her nest on a rocky ledge, sometimes at a considerable height above the ground.

Not infrequently a nest will be built on the face of a steep embankment. To provide a niche in which to secure the nest, the female digs away the earth with her claws, using her breast to round off the freshly exposed soil. It is really quite impressive to see the bird at work in this manner. Later, as the nest begins to take shape, she again uses her breast as a "forming tool" to ensure that the cavity has a smooth rounded surface.

The nest usually takes about a month to build, and some birds appear to prefer to work on the nest in the morning. In any case, the building period is one of feverish activity for the female, while she is actually working. Once I observed a bird gathering nesting material and transporting it, always by the same route. This entailed ascending a slope, springing on to a low branch of a large sassafras tree which collapsed many years previously, running along the branch to the trunk, following the trunk to another rising branch and then gliding from the high point across to the centre of a tall tree fern. She made twenty-four trips in an hour and did not cease running for more than a few moments.

Busy female lyrebirds are not above accepting a helping hand. Once I placed a large ringtail possum's nest (which had been discarded by its owner) in the path of a lyrebird (Droopy, see p. 110), which was building her nest. Within two days she had incorporated the whole of the possum's nest in her new home. There is much evidence to suggest that frequently a lyrebird will re-use the lining from one of her old nests.

In areas where the lyrebirds are not disturbed by predators, they build close to the ground. The large size of the nest makes this the obvious site, but there is no doubt that the intrusion of human beings, cats, dogs and foxes into their haunts has forced the lyrebirds (in Sherbrooke, anyway) to build at considerable heights. In recent years there have been many high nests, even up to eighty feet above the ground.

A large nest in the fork of a musk tree (Olearia argophylla)

Female lyrebird flying away from a seventy-foot high nest in a sassafras tree.

Building at such a height entails a great deal of extra work for the female, because every stick has to be transported in her beak. Being a poor flier, the bird leaps off the ground on to a low limb and then springs from bough to bough, zigzagwise, until she is high enough to glide across or down to the nest site.

Later on, the food is transported to the chick in the same manner. It is a thrilling experience to see the bird, after she has fed the chick, launch herself into space and glide gracefully down to earth through the trees. Usually she follows a wide sweep and one can hear the "swish" as she descends. On nearing the ground, however, she uses her wings as brakes and alights gently. Her quest for food commences again immediately she reaches the ground.

Although the female lyrebird builds her nest in the same area year after year, only once have I found the same nest used twice in successive years. On two other occasions, the same nesting site has been used again, once after an interval of two years and once after a period of five years.

Not infrequently the bird will construct a "cradle", that is, the basic structure of the nest, and then abandon it. She may even build two cradles, before finally selecting the site. Occasionally, she will return to an old cradle in a subsequent year and complete the nest.

The birds mate, usually, early in June and the egg is laid early in July. There are, however, early and late starters. Once I saw a female gathering sticks in mid-February, but she gave the impression that she was playing with them rather than seriously interested in nest-building. Nevertheless, in 1939, another female had her nest practically

Spotty paying a visit to Droopy's nest.

complete by the end of April, although thereafter she followed the normal schedule, the chick leaving the nest towards the end of September. On another occasion, the nest had not been completed by the end of the first week in July, yet the chick hatched out early in September. Another female, in 1947, brought out her chick in the last week of September, and was even more retarded in her 1955 schedule, the chick not leaving the nest until the 16th November. In other years she was more or less normal. More recently (1963), a chick was found in a nest on 1st December; it was almost ready to leave.

While the male does not participate in nest-building, he may occasionally, accidentally or by design, show an interest in the nest. Mrs. McPherson once photographed Spotty peering inquisitively into the nest of "Droopy" who built in his territory in 1960.

When the female is ready to lay, she plucks the soft downy grey feathers from her own body to line the nest. A single egg is laid to each clutch; it is grey with purple splotches and is similar in size to that of a domestic hen.

Only one egg is laid each year; the weight varies from $1\frac{3}{4}$ to $2\frac{1}{4}$ oz., the dimensions being $2.6''\pm$ x $1.73''\pm$. The egg of the Albert Lyrebird is slightly smaller, i.e. $2.5''\pm$ x $1.66''\pm$.

The egg shows a wide range of colour variation, some eggs being as dark as slate while others are light greyish-black. The splotches likewise vary in colour. A museum specimen of the egg of an Edward Lyrebird, from the Stanthorpe district in Queensland, was almost white in colour and distinctly smaller than any other lyrebird egg seen to date.

While it is generally considered that the lyrebird lays only one egg each year (and my own experience in Sherbrooke confirms this view), the late A. J. Campbell reports several instances (somewhat vague) of two eggs having been found in the one nest at the same time. Unfortunately, the eggs were stolen by collectors and so all chance of obtaining information regarding the original ownership of the two eggs and of the possibility of there being two chicks in the one nest was destroyed.

As incubation proceeds, the number of feathers is increased, so that when the chick hatches out there is a soft warm bed ready. While the normal period of incubation is forty-two days, in some cases, successful incubations have extended to fifty days. In the case of infertile eggs, the female has been known to sit for nine weeks.

August in the lyrebird's habitat is always cold and, while the chick is very young, the mother returns to the nest to sleep with him until he is about three-and-a-half weeks old; but after that the nest is not large enough to house them both and the female roosts in a tree nearby.

While the female is brooding, her tail takes on a kink, and on several occasions such birds have been stalked to their nests — though not without some difficulty.

Lyrebird chick, aged four weeks, at entrance to nest.

70

Kink in the tail of a female lyrebird during the incubation period.

During the time the chick is in the nursery, his devoted mother is very brave and does not hesitate to attack any creature, human or otherwise, which dares to approach too close to the nest. I remember still how surprised — afraid, in fact, for my eyes — I was when a female lyrebird flew at me and trailed her long claws through my hair! But not all the birds are so bold and, after the first excitement, the female usually settles down and accepts the stranger, provided he does not venture too close to the nest.

Some birds are much less tolerant than others in this regard. Once my wife and I were visiting a nest built on a rocky ledge about a foot above the water in a little creek, not far from the spot where I had found my first nest several years previously. We were incautious enough to alarm the female, which bounded about from tree-fern to creek bed, making a terrific din in her excitement. Suddenly she was joined by a second and much larger female, and the two of them made a tremendous commotion. We retired, of course — it was the only thing to do — and peace was restored. Many other females have been much more friendly and have even followed me around as I dug up worms for them in the forest.

The growing chick seems almost always to be hungry and is fed, on an average, about once every half hour. The female gathers the food over a fairly wide area and the numerous scratchings in the area adjacent to the nest are evidence of her industry. The chick's food consists of worms, grubs, centipedes and little crustaceans which abound in the damp soil beneath the rocks and logs. The female stores the food in her cheek pouches and partly digests it before she returns to the nest. Before actually feeding the chick, she tops off with worms, which may often be seen wriggling furiously in her beak.

When she is ready to feed the chick, the female approaches the nest and, after making a soft clucking noise to warn the young one of her presence, springs on to the

A threat display from a female lyrebird with a chick in the nest.

Lyrebird chick, approximately twelve days old.

platform at the entrance to the nest. The chick opens its mouth wide, whereupon the female thrusts in her beak and delivers the food parcel.

When the chick has been fed, the mother pauses for a short period on the platform and makes soft clucking noises which the chick appears to understand quite well. As the chick has to live in the nest for six weeks, it can be readily appreciated that nest hygiene is very important in the domestic life of the lyrebird. If Nature calls, as it does on an average about once every hour, or after every second feed, the chick, encouraged by the noises made by its mother, turns round in the nest and delivers a dropping directly into her beak. The dropping is contained in a tough gelatinous sac, which facilitates transportation. This instinctive behaviour of the chick, of course, commences from the time it breaks out of the egg, blind and helpless. If the nest is near a stream the female, sometimes running and sometimes gliding, carries the dropping to it and, wading out into the water, very deliberately submerges it before departing. If there is no stream handy, she digs a hole and buries the dropping in the ground. Thus is the scent destroyed and the danger from the birds' natural enemies minimised.

Apart from the vocal communications between mother and chick at meal times, the chick and female are normally silent. This is an obvious protective arrangement; but, if an intruder ventures too close to the nest, he is liable to be greeted by a resounding squawk which is calculated to chill the bravest heart. The effect is startling, and I can still recall (nowadays I may even risk a quiet chuckle) the discomfiture of a young friend of mine who was making her first acquaintance with a lyrebird chick whose shrill cry caused her to lose her footing and slide down a steep muddy embankment into a pool of water in the gully below!

However, if one can overcome the first feelings of alarm and places one's hand in the nest and strokes the chick's head gently, it ceases to squawk and purrs like a cat before a fire. Apparently the soft pressure of the hand induces the soothing effect produced by the mother's warm body and the chick's fears are allayed.

Once the chick leaves the nest, however, obviously these friendly overtures are no longer possible, and the chick loudly proclaims his annoyance with any intruder who ventures into his domain.

During the interval between meals, the little chick preens himself and disposes of the white pieces of skin which are constantly flaking off his growing body. He also takes exercise and then, having satisfied himself on these two items, nestles down in his soft feathery bed and goes to sleep. As with other juveniles, as the chick matures, he needs less sleep, and may sometimes be observed catching mosquitoes, which are always

Lyrebird chick, four weeks old, "purrs" softly when stroked on the back.

Lyrebird chick approximately three-and-a-half weeks old. The white spots are pieces of skin which are continually flaking off the growing body.

troublesome in September. His expression of satisfaction when he makes a catch is most impressive!

The chick is born practically naked, having only a few long black hair-like feathers, but within a week has acquired a coat of sooty-coloured down. The eyes open at about this time, also. Later, as the feathers proper begin to grow, the colour becomes lighter and, by the time the chick is six weeks old, he has lost practically all semblance of down and has ordinary feathers. His tail is about three-and-a-half to five inches long and his throat has a distinct rufous patch on it.

Usually, when the nest is quite close to the ground, the chick is eager to leave, sometimes even before he is six weeks old, but in other instances there may be some reluctance on his part to leave a comfortable home. In such a case the mother withholds his food, so that eventually he leaves the nest in order to investigate the cause of the delay in the arrival of his meal.

I once had a very good demonstration of this "starving out" technique. Early one morning, on my way to visit a nest which was situated in a musk tree, some twenty-five feet above the ground, I was picking my way from rock to rock down the creek when I came upon a collection of six droppings in a little pool. This clearly indicated that there was a nest close by, but I could not spend time in searching because it was necessary for me to be at the other nest at a particular time in order to take advantage of whatever light there might be for the few minutes when the nest was not in shadow. Returning

Lyrebird's nest.

Friendly female approaching nest to feed Red Blue.

Lyrebird chick, six weeks old, ready to leave nest. Whilst standing at entrance to nest, awaiting his mother's return with food, he yawned.

Female lyrebird taking dropping from chick. Occasionally the female swallows the dropping.

Female lyrebird taking dropping to the creek.

some two hours later, I was interested to see that there were still only six droppings in the pool. Having satisfied myself that there were no fresh droppings above or below the pool, I surmised that the female was endeavouring to starve the chick out of the nest or that he had in fact already left. Experience of past years enabled me to make a reasonable guess at the probable direction in which the nest lay and I proceeded very cautiously to look for it. It was about forty yards from the creek and, when I was about half way towards it, the chick, hearing me approaching, flew out with a loud squawk. Obviously he was just "rearing to go" and needed only a slight impulse to precipitate his departure.

There is some evidence that chicks remain in high nests for a period longer than six weeks; one chick which was reared in a nest eighty feet above the ground was still in the nest at the age of eight weeks.

The descent would certainly be fraught with some peril and apparently the chick was restrained in some mysterious manner.

During 1948 to 1950 I had under observation an immature male lyrebird with a broken wing which may have been sustained when he left a high nest.

The period during which the chick is sitting helpless in the nest must be one of considerable anxiety for the mother bird and, as soon as he leaves the nursery, he is coaxed away from the vicinity of the nest. He is "planted" in some safe place — in the shadow of a large log, in sword grass, or in some other place where he will not be conspicuous. The mother then continues for some time to feed him, just as she has during the previous six weeks. It is noteworthy that at this stage the dropping is no

A female lyrebird, sitting in the nest, upon her chick, her beak loaded with worms.

A "friendly" female lyrebird approaches cautiously, but without alarm, to feed the hungry chick held by my wife.

longer enveloped, as there is no further need to protect the nest, nor are any other precautions taken. The chick, of course, changes his hiding place frequently as he follows his mother about.

The female continues to feed the chick for several months after he has left the nest. While he thus enjoys the services of his devoted mother, the chick learns to spring off the forest floor on to low branches, then to "climb" higher into trees, so as to avoid his ground enemies. His mother continues to gather food and store it in her cheek pouches before climbing laboriously up the tree to the chick. Sometimes the chick will move from one tree to another between feeds and his poor mother has to search for him all over again. By the time he is four to five months old, he is probably not winning more

The feeding process complete.

Hungry chick opens beak wide to enable mother lyrebird to deliver food parcel.

than twenty per cent of his own food, but from now on he spends more time on the ground close to his mother which gradually teaches him where to search for food.

Whilst mother and chick may be joined in summer by other plaintails, including no doubt brothers and sisters of previous years, the bond between the two birds is very strong and they remain closely associated until May or even later, when the mother leaves the chick to undertake a new round of domestic chores. The youngster, accustomed even as late as May or June to receiving tidbits from his mother, now begs from his older brothers and sisters, which resemble his mother in appearance. It is a moving experience to see the young bird begging, only to be pushed aside by an older bird's claws. The youngster soon learns that he must fend for himself and takes his place with other plaintails.

In some cases the mother-chick bond proves very difficult for the female to break. In one instance, a female, now with another chick in the nest, was observed flying and running at her year-old offspring, endeavouring to drive it away. As soon as the female's back was turned the youngster intruded again, hoping to be fed by his mother. In yet another case, a female returning to the nest, her cheek pouches bulging with food for the new season's chick, was waylaid by a hungry one-year-old chick. His persistent begging, no doubt intensified by the sight of worms wriggling in his mother's beak, caused the poor mother to give him the entire food parcel!

It would seem that this begging behaviour may remain latent even in older birds, but may manifest itself under favourable conditions. Once (December 1962) I watched a five-year-old male lyrebird ardently displaying to another male two years younger. The latter, whilst listening intently, preened himself throughout the serenading. The older bird then approached him and began to beg vigorously. After several minutes

80

the younger bird regurgitated what appeared to be a partly digested worm, which was promptly picked up and eaten by the other bird. The two of them then strolled away into the forest together.

It appears not to be well known that the female lyrebird is quite a good songster, often rivalling the male. Her repertoire is extensive and her mimicry perfect. She frequently bursts into melody when preening herself after a bath and, strange as it may seem, when she is concerned for the safety of her chick. This no doubt is a case of "distraction behaviour".

One particular female lyrebird in Sherbrooke Forest, which was renowned for her prowess as a songster, was known as the "Singing Hen". She had another pronounced male characteristic, namely, that of displaying on logs and on branches of trees, especially when she was excited by the presence of a human intruder near her nest. Another bird, though not given to displaying, used to sing beautifully during periods of stress.

Although the female lyrebird devotes a great deal of her time to winning food for her hungry chick, she nevertheless does not neglect her toilet and may be seen to visit a favourite perch to preen her feathers, several times during the day.

She may also at times be subject to conflicting emotions. Once I saw a female returning to her chick, with her cheek pouches laden with worms. She was also seen by an adolescent male (not her mate) which immediately threw his tail over his head and began to display to her. The "devoted mother" responded coquettishly to his overtures but after a minute or so appeared to become aware again that she had other duties to perform and ran to the nest to feed the chick.

Female lyrebird enticing six-weeks-old chick to leave the nest.

9
IMMATURE LYREBIRDS

WHEN THE TIME ARRIVES for the female lyrebird to begin her preparations for the year's work, the chick from the previous year remains with the other immature birds. One may frequently see little groups of three, four, five and sometimes more, immature male and female lyrebirds in company together in the forest. They live as a group, seeking their food, singing and playing together.

The immature males and females are practically indistinguishable. It is sometimes stated that the immature male may be distinguished by the rufous patch under the chin, and it is certainly true that the immature birds are thus characterized, but I always find it difficult to decide, on this evidence alone, which are the females and which are the males. The immature birds of both sexes have the same sort of tails, which consist of plain broad feathers, as with the adult female. In both cases, by the time the bird is four years old, the rufous patch is barely discernible and it is not visible in mature birds.

At the age of one year the young lyrebird has a tail consisting of two short lyrates having the characteristic "V"-markings, together with fourteen plain fully webbed

Young male raising tail preparatory to display.

Rear view of young male lyrebird displaying. Note the first- and second-generation plain feathers, wide medians and immature lyrates. Filamentation has not yet commenced.

feathers, the two central ones (medians) being longer than the others, which have somewhat "sharp" ends.

The three different types of feathers — two lyrates, two medians and twelve plain ones — undergo a sequence of changes by moulting and replacement in a most interesting manner. The moults are usually not synchronized: that is, one of the lyrates (first generation) may be shed and replaced by a second-generation lyrate while the other first-generation lyrate is retained for several months, and this out-of-phase relationship between the lyrates may continue until the bird is almost or quite mature. In successive generations of lyrates, the "V"s (windows) become deeper and more clearly defined,

The beginning of filamentation.

and the ends become darker and more club-like, so that each new feather more closely resembles its ultimate form, i.e., the lyrates of the mature male lyrebird.

Likewise the medians are moulted and replaced by a new pair (not always in phase), the second generation medians being longer and more tapering than the first set. Usually, by the time the bird is four or five years old, he will have acquired his "adolescent" medians (third generation) which more closely resemble the medians of the mature bird, in that they contain some short filaments on the outer side of the shaft. In due course these are moulted and replaced by a pair of fine whip-like (post-adolescent) medians which have only very short barbs on the inner side of the shaft while the outer side

Immature male lyrebird displaying, showing three plain feathers, left.

Crossed Lyrates showing lyre pattern.

84

A close-up view of an immature male lyrebird displaying, showing the growing feathers.

Changeling lyrebird displaying.

Double White displaying tail.

carries somewhat longer (though still short) filaments (barbs). The medians of older mature birds have short filaments on both sides of the distal end of the shaft, the greater part of the shaft being practically devoid of barbs.

The twelve plain feathers likewise undergo development by moulting and replacement over a period of perhaps three to five years, the lives of the individual first- (and second-) generation plain feathers showing considerable variation, so that the tail consists of three types of feathers covering a range of generations. The first-generation plain feathers may readily be distinguished from the second; the former have rather pointed ends while the latter are distinctly rounded.

When the young male lyrebird is in his fourth or fifth year, the plain feathers become thinner due to the loss of barbicels and one such feather may even shed barbs to produce a filamented feather. Frequently several such feathers may be seen in the tail of the young lyrebird, though the tail feathers of some adolescent lyrebirds appear not to undergo this filamentation process.

Ultimately, one or more of these feathers is moulted and replaced by a new feather which grows as an (adolescent) filamentary from the beginning. Thus the principal part of the young lyrebird's tail (i.e. excluding the lyrates and medians) may consist of

An immature male lyrebird at an advanced stage of adolescence, still retaining two unfilamented tail feathers.

Immature male lyrebird displaying, showing adolescent medians, plain, unchanged feathers, filamentaries and out-of-phase lyrates.

"plain" second-generation feathers of different ages, changing feathers (due to loss of barbicels) and filamentary feathers grown as such from the beginning.

When the changes in these twelve feathers are considered in conjunction with the changes in the other two types of feathers, it can readily be appreciated that the tail of the changeling lyrebird presents a most interesting appearance over a period of several years. Moreover each bird has its own time sequence of moults and replacements, so that generalizations become very difficult to make.

Ultimately, however, usually in his seventh or eighth year, the immature male lyrebird sheds all his tail feathers and grows a new one consisting of sixteen feathers — two lyrates, two medians and twelve filamentaries — in the respective forms of the

Immature male lyrebird showing out-of-phase medians, one pre-adolescent and one adolescent type, plain (unfilamented) feathers, filamented feathers and adolescent lyrates.

mature bird. Frequently, however, they are not all in phase and a further moult may be necessary to bring all feathers into the same generation. The male lyrebird will usually be approximately eight years old before he is fully mature, as judged by his tail. Whether he will succeed in winning a mate in his first year will depend among other things on whether he matured in time to compete with the other mature males during the mating season.

During the transition period, the immature birds pay much attention to singing and displaying — that is, in September, October and right through summer and autumn. They use their own mounds, which are frequently, but not always, less elaborate than those of the adult birds.

Throughout adolescence immature lyrebirds form "partnerships" which may last for a day or longer, after which period both partners may become associated with other plaintails; while, at a later date, the original partners may become re-united. In other words, the birds are promiscuous.

During the partnership, the one bird will display and sing ardently to the other and the two will follow one another through the forest for long periods. While one bird is displaying, the other will frequently run on to the mound and endeavour to get under the other bird's tail. This behaviour occurs with immature birds definitely known to be males, though in some cases females may be involved.

It is a moving experience to see two immature lyrebirds on the same mound with their tails erected and touching while the birds circle and sing together. Such duets occasionally continue for a short period after the birds have fully matured, but the partnership appears to be dissolved upon their taking mates for themselves. However, it is by no means uncommon for an adult male in full plumage (and even in moult) to visit another which is displaying on the mound. In such cases, the display is usually soon terminated and the birds chase one another through the forest for several minutes before separating. Sometimes two or three fully-plumed adult males may be seen playing "chasey" through the forest. It seems probable that such games are the continuation of early friendships. Juvenile and adolescent lyrebirds also exhibit this behaviour.

The prelude to this game of "chasey" is most interesting: a lyrebird may be scratching for food, preening on a stump or branch, displaying, or doing any of the acts lyrebirds normally do, when his acute hearing tells him that another lyrebird is

Male lyrebird suspecting the presence of another lyrebird. This bird was in moult and growing a new tail. The beginnings of a lyrate can be seen.

The same bird as in the previous picture, but three weeks later.

Immature male lyrebird (five-and-a-half years) singing and displaying to fern, showing head moult.

Immature male lyrebird displaying, showing out-of-phase lyrates, three incompletely filamented juvenile feathers, post-adolescent filamentaries and post-adolescent medians.

approaching. Both birds, though unable to see one another, will then be observed to press their tails against the earth, stretch their necks and make snake-like movements with their heads. As the intruder approaches within sight of the other bird, the reptilian behaviour continues until, suddenly, one bird darts at the other and the chase begins.

During adolescence young lyrebirds frequently display to inanimate objects such as fern fronds, sticks, low stumps or bracken ferns. They pirouette before the object of their devotions, singing and going through the motions of their elaborate dance. Sometimes, too, they will display to a blackbird or grey thrush which happens to alight near the spot where they are feeding or singing. It almost seems as if they must have an audience and their hormone system responds to almost any favourable stimulus to induce a display.

Once I made a "model" out of several pieces of wood and masonite. The general shape was fairly true and the head quite life-like, except that it was flat. The "wings" consisted of several feathers I had picked up in the forest, and the tail contained a few feathers including several of a kookaburra! Nevertheless, the presentation of this model to a number of the birds induced display.

Even Spotty was a victim of the hoax, but not for long. His behaviour suggested that the subject of the display (receiver) normally gives some form of recognition to the displayer. This was obviously not forthcoming from the model and Spotty walked over and gave it a clout with his claw before stalking off in quest of more responsive admirers.

Immature lyrebirds exhibit a peculiar behaviour which does not appear to have any logical explanation. Several birds may be feeding a little distance apart, but in company, or a bird may be alone, when suddenly it will utter a loud squawk and jump up in the air and begin to run in a circle. It springs on to the side of a tree, perhaps five or six feet above the ground, and "bounces" off it, thus striking half a dozen trees or so in its circuit. After four or five rounds, during which time it continues its peculiar squawking, it suddenly returns to normal and resumes feeding. The bird appears to enjoy the experience, and one is reminded of a puppy or a kitten playing a game, or perhaps a lamb frisking in a field. If the bird were alarmed, it would immediately leave the area, and its call note would be quite different. Perhaps it is just a game. Other birds e.g. magpies, play games, so why not lyrebirds?

It has been observed that the young birds do not appreciate the intrusion of an adult bird into their private affairs, particularly where a young female or young male is concerned. On one occasion, in September, I was watching a group of four young birds, one of which was paying court to a young plaintail. Suddenly "Timothy" came along. Now Timothy was over twenty years old at the time and, assuming that he *had* a mate, would have mated months previously. To my surprise, he began openly to make advances to the young plaintail. The immature male increased the tempo of his wooing, whereupon Timothy sprang up in the air and struck the young bird with both claws on the breast, almost knocking him over. The youngster darted off, but soon returned and stood balefully regarding his larger opponent for quite a while. He was obviously trying to make up his mind whether to attack or not and he watched Timothy very carefully. He made as if to go forward on several occasions, but was restrained by a slight intimidatory gesture from Timothy and eventually, concluding that discretion was the better part of valour, withdrew.

Two immature males displaying to one another.

10

LYREBIRD PERSONALITIES

FROM THE RECORDS AVAILABLE, it would appear that the first lyrebird to become a recognized "personality" was "Old Jack", a bird which was caught shortly after leaving the nest in October 1885, and which lived for the next nineteen-and-a-half years as a free-roving bird, on the farm property of the McNeilly family near Drouin, in west Gippsland, Victoria.

Jack, who soon became a great favourite, had free access to the house as well as to a gully adjoining the homestead. He would sometimes wander away by day, once as far as three miles from "home", but always returned by night. He was so friendly that he frequently got in the way of the farm employees from whom, it is reported, he learned the expression "Look out, Jack". It appears that there was no sound heard in the farmyard which he could not imitate: the noise of a horse and dray moving slowly with the play of the wheels and the axle boxes, chains rattling, an occasional "Gee up Bess", the sounds of the violin, piano, cornet, cross-cut saw, the squeal of a pig being slaughtered, a dog howling, a child crying and, of course, all the bird calls in the area.

In the early thirties, Mr. and Mrs. Jack Coyle of Springwood, in the Blue Mountains, New South Wales, reared a pair of lyrebird chicks, taken from the nests as fledgelings. "Joe" (the male) and "Zoe" (the female) became very tame and gained much publicity through being photographed with a variety of glamorous overseas admirers (and no doubt local ones). "Joe" and "Zoe" teamed to produce "Pat", the first lyrebird known to have been bred in captivity. Through a series of unfortunate accidents, these three birds died prematurely, though "Joe" and "Zoe" enjoyed an association of fifteen years.

Whereas "Jack" had been a free-roving bird who, by force of circumstances beyond his control, had become, in a sense, domesticated through a life-long attachment to a farm, "Joe" and "Zoe" knew only the life of an aviary.

Quite different was the case of "James", who has been immortalized by Ambrose Pratt in his *Lore of the Lyrebird*. This was the first book I ever read on the lyrebird and, although I do not now accept all that Mr. Pratt's experienced pen then wrote, I still derive great pleasure from that book and meeting "James" in its pages.

"James" was a bird which lived freely in Sherbrooke Forest, at the Ferny Creek end, and "adopted" a resident, Mrs. Edith Wilkinson in whose garden and about whose home he freely disported himself, feeding, singing and displaying.

Male lyrebird (Timothy) pauses during early morning quest for food.

Mrs. Wilkinson first became aware of James's interest in her garden in February 1930, and there developed a mutual respect and understanding between these two creatures, one human, one avian, which Pratt described as "A Miracle of the Dandenongs".

As a result of this remarkable association, by courtesy of Mrs. Wilkinson, James performed before many of Australia's leading ornithologists and scientific observers; he was filmed and his voice was broadcast over the radio.

James disappeared in 1943 and, as he would have been at least 20 or 21 years old, it must be presumed that he died. Let us hope it was from natural causes.

I was not privileged to meet any of the celebrities referred to above; but, over a period exceeding thirty years, have come to know some of the lyrebirds of Sherbrooke Forest as distinct personalities.

The first of these was a bird known as "Timothy", who was "King of the Forest" from 1936 to 1953 and who was the first of the more approachable lyrebirds of Sherbrooke. While his neighbour "Jock" was frequently heard exercising his magnificent voice (sometimes as a soloist, but oftentimes in a duet with Timothy), it was only through extreme caution that one was ever permitted to approach within sight of this beautiful bird; Timothy by contrast seemed to enjoy the company of his human admirers. Sometimes as I sat on the floor of the forest near him, he would be so absorbed in his quest for food that he appeared to become oblivious to my presence as he moved slowly toward me, so much so that on more than one occasion, when he made a sudden movement, I had to duck my head to avoid having my face swished by his tail!

Timothy was often admired by visitors from overseas, especially by American soldiers during World War II. He had a very extensive repertoire — probably, I think, the best of all the lyrebirds of Sherbrooke — and his loud ringing notes could be heard at a distance of several hundred yards.

Timothy and Jock would often meet at the margin of their territories and engage in a game of chasey, during which they coursed round and round emitting peculiar grunting noises, until after perhaps a quarter of an hour they would separate and almost invariably, in consequence of their mutual stimulation, they displayed and sang with enhanced fervour.

Sometimes they would be joined in their game by a bob-tailed lyrebird (a mature male which had moulted his tail) and it amuses me still to recall one particular occasion when Timothy was displaying on a mound, when Bobtail, who had been standing nearby, suddenly sprang over the fringe of bracken fern and landed on the mound in front of Timothy. The latter gave a loud squawk and began to chase the intruder. It soon became clear that this was no game and that Timothy was really annoyed with Bobtail, whom he pursued in wide circles up and down the slope. The surprising thing was that Bobtail could easily have flown away (because without his long tail a male lyrebird can fly very swiftly), but no doubt his fear of Timothy prevented him from indulging in what would have been an unusual activity for him. Poor Bobtail's knees wobbled and he staggered, but Timothy kept the pressure on him. Suddenly the Old Master abandoned Bobtail and ran to a patch of bracken a hundred yards away where he immediately began to display and sing ecstatically. I arrived a little out of breath, but managed to collect some very good photographs.

Reference has been made on page 16 to the making of a recording of the lyrebird's song. Perhaps it was not altogether fair, but later in the same day, out of curiosity, we played that recording back, in Timothy's territory. It was a tribute to the quality of the recording that within seconds, Timothy came running up the hill to make the acquaintance of the intruder. He stalked around the tape recorder, with his head on one side, obviously puzzled. This was clearly a new experience — he had never seen a lyrebird like this before. When the machine was turned off, he gazed at the strange device for a few moments and then slowly made his way back to the gully below.

A second playing brought him up again; this time he circled the machine, walked up and gave it a push with his claws, and then resumed feeding, still puzzled, a short distance away.

When the machine was played a third time, he looked across, but did not bother to investigate. He had learned that at all events, it was not a rival lyrebird!

I can still recall my last day with Timothy — 13th September, 1953. I had for companions on this occasion a lady and her son who was in delicate health, who had come over three hundred miles from the dry mallee country in north-western Victoria in the hope of catching a fleeting glimpse of the lyrebird. We had stood patiently for an hour as Timothy fed: scratch, scratch, duck the head, pick up a worm; scratch, scratch, duck the head, pick up a worm . . . The robins had come and fed with him and chased away the hungry little scrub-wrens which had hopped hopefully between his legs; a pilot bird had joined him and called loudly "I'll give you a guinea a week", but there were no takers . . . Timothy had stood with dignity upon a stump and preened . . . and then, oh blessed moment, he had run to a mound in the ferns and displayed to the accompaniment of his own melodious rhapsody. The boy stood enraptured — lips parted and eyes aglow; finally he turned to his mother and said, "Mummy, we must come back with Daddy; he'd love to see Timothy".

At last Timothy left the mound and the party broke up. At half-past three, on that same day, I stood once again beneath the Master of Song as he poured forth his melody from a favourite singing perch. I did not know then that I was not to see Timothy again. He was just over a quarter of a century old — but the memory of this gay Prince of Mocking Birds lingers on.

In 1950, I became acquainted with another lyrebird who was to become a special attraction for my camera over the next fourteen years. This was "Spotty", so called because of the white spots (three on the breast and two on the back of his neck) which distinguished him with certainty from other lyrebirds. Spotty settled down in the territory formerly occupied by Jock, who had disappeared about 1950.

In the winter of 1953, I had seen Spotty and Timothy engaged in duets and once was enchanted by the spectacle of these two beautiful birds standing six feet apart facing one another and singing in full voice. The thought occurred to me then that this was a challenge and, indeed, in the season following Timothy's death, Spotty was in command of Timothy's territory. Here he remained until the autumn of 1964, when he disappeared. He was then approximately twenty-one or twenty-two years old.

Yellow-breasted Robin feeding young ones.

Portrait of Spotty, taken from thirty inches.

Spotty suspecting presence of another bird.

Spotty was much more approachable even than Timothy. I frequently sat no more than two feet away from him and for several years spent almost every week-end in his company. He would come to me when I called and was altogether a charming and lovable companion.

Spotty was not only a very fine songster; he was an accomplished musician. He had a wide repertoire, though perhaps not so extensive a one as Timothy's, and undoubtedly derived much pleasure — dare one say satisfaction? — from his singing. He had a number of his own improvisations of the melodious calls of the grey thrush and his own variants of the call of the whip bird and pilot bird. These variants were not accidental, due to an imperfect recollection of the call of the bird whose notes he was imitating; they were rendered consciously as examples of his consummate skill and artistry as a musician.

Spotty always moulted earlier than most other male lyrebirds in the area; he moulted either late in August or early in September, and grew a new tail during the next twelve weeks. When in moult, he looked rather forlorn; but, as his tail grew, he would occasionally sing and even display, whilst in the company of the immature birds with whom he spent much of his time. I took advantage of this association to locate him during this period, when his own voice was largely silent. The immature males at this time were highly vocal.

Because Spotty was so friendly, it was possible to follow him closely and record much of his behaviour photographically. In this way a great deal of interesting information was obtained.

Lyrebirds, with their very acute hearing, are able to intercept notes far beyond the

99

"Oh! Were you calling me?" Male lyrebird receives a message from one of his neighbours in the forest.

human auditory range, so that they frequently react to sounds which the human observer does not hear. Sometimes Spotty would be feeding or preening when he would suddenly receive a message, and one learned to tell from his behaviour at such times what had evoked the reaction. He would look with surprise in the direction from which the message had come and remain in a tense attitude for perhaps a minute or more. Sometimes he would resume his feeding or preening; at other times he would run quickly towards the source of the message. Frequently on such occasions one would follow him for a hundred yards or so to find a young lyrebird standing or silently displaying on a mound; at Spotty's approach he would leave the mound hastily, though with obvious reluctance. At other times, Spotty would utter a peculiar whimpering note, expressing doubt or concern. Once I was trailing Spotty when I saw his crest rise and heard him

100

utter a note of concern — "Aw-kok" — at the same instant as the small birds of the forest set up a cacophony and began to dive-bomb an owl in a large tree. Spotty could not possibly have seen the owl, but must have intercepted a note emitted by this bird, which was inaudible to human ears.

Once on a sunny Saturday afternoon I was watching a group of lyrebirds, including Spotty; they were simply feeding, pausing now and then to release a burst of song. Suddenly they "dived for cover" and froze. I was watching Spotty particularly and saw him sheltering, immobile, under some dead fronds still attached to a large tree-fern. He was tense and motionless.

Just a split second after the birds scattered, I heard the "kee-kee-kee" call of a large bird of prey (a goshawk, I think, it was) and saw its shadow on the ground as it passed overhead.

The birds could not possibly have seen that bird before they dispersed so rapidly, but they had obviously received a high frequency note which they associated instinctively with predators.

After a short while, the lyrebirds gradually relaxed and resumed their normal activities. The interesting sequel to this episode is that, within a few weeks, Spotty and all the other lyrebirds in this area were imitating the goshawk to perfection!

Spotty, like other lyrebirds, would take a drink from a curved piece of bark which had collected a little rain or dew overnight; but he had his favourite refreshment bars. One of these was a large knobby tree root which projected above ground-level and which had rotted out in the centre; another was a hollow formed within the base of a tall mountain ash. Sometimes Spotty would feel the need of a drink when he was a

Spotty drinking from a pool in the base of a hollow mountain ash.

considerable distance from his drinking bowls and one could tell from "the look on his face" what he had in mind. He would go straight to the water; but, if he happened to be passing a particular wombat burrow, he would always run down into it before proceeding. He was not alone in his curiosity about wombat burrows.

While Spotty seemed to enjoy the company of the robins, scrub wrens and pilot birds (all small birds) at his meal table, he always kept a wary eye on the wily old kookaburra which frequently perched on a nearby branch, with his greedy eyes watching for Spotty to uncover a large worm. When this happened, the kookaburra would fly in like a dive-bomber and knock Spotty, or any other lyrebird he had been watching, sideways. One often saw feathers fall from the poor lyrebird when the bully struck it.

The small birds had no fear of Spotty and his kind, and would hop about between his legs fossicking for tidbits. Occasionally a robin would alight for an instant on Spotty's back! Sometimes the little birds would find themselves accidentally walked upon; but, though they uttered tiny squeaks, they never took fright. Once I saw a robin hop towards a little stick at the same instant as Spotty's claws reached out to remove it; his claws closed round the robin, which was thrown through the air for several feet. The small bird opened his wings and alighted like a tiny grey and yellow parachute, and was back in Spotty's worm patch within the minute. I had been sitting with Spotty and a pair of robins for several hours, hoping to take a photograph of the trio, and I was fortunately able to get the shot of the robin in Spotty's claws. One might well say, "This was a scoop!"

Spotty singing, while a pair of Yellow-breasted Robins hopefully watch his worm patch for a tidbit.

One of my most amusing recollections of Spotty is the memory of this gay character standing on a log along which a colony of ants had established a supply line. On becoming aware of the ants, Spotty cocked his head on one side and sized the situation up. Then he stretched out his neck and opened his beak which he pushed along as far as he could, scooping up the ants.

Standing still, he consumed this first harvest before repeating the performance. He obviously enjoyed the change of diet and remained at the one spot for several minutes, during which time he must have consumed several hundred ants.

In 1959 and 1960, I made tape recordings of Spotty's song. To do this, it was necessary to lay out 500 yards of flex from a nearby guest house, the celebrated "Sherbrooke Lodge", to Spotty's display area. I had 100 yards of flex "free"; that is, out of the densely forested area, so that I could approach close to any one of several of Spotty's mounds. I used a three-speed tape recorder with a moving coil microphone, which was so sensitive that it was possible to record the Gang-gang cockatoos feeding in the crowns of the mountain ash trees, over 150 feet above the ground. It was necessary to use a wheelbarrow to transport the equipment, which consisted of the recorder, microphone and photographic gear; but the end result was worthwhile.

In the winter of 1963, a young male lyrebird intruded into Spotty's territory, just as Spotty had invaded Timothy's domain ten years earlier. I wondered then whether Spotty's end was approaching and it was not really surprising that, when the 1964 opera season opened in Lyrebird Land, Spotty was no longer the star. But nobody who knew him will ever forget him and he will live on in my memory forever.

Somewhat surprisingly however, during the winter of 1964, Spotty's territory was occupied not by the 1963 intruder but by a very engaging male lyrebird in the final

Spotty accidentally catches a robin in his claw; fortunately, the little bird was not harmed.

stages of adolescence. He bore such a striking resemblance to Spotty — his voice, size and shape of tail and head — that one is strongly tempted to believe that he is in fact one of Spotty's sons. He could be Spotty's 1956 offspring. There are now (September, 1966) several birds in this area whose form, behaviour and voice proclaim them as Spotty's progeny. Indeed, as one hears the tremulous notes from beyond, it is sometimes difficult to realize that it is not actually Spotty himself. Thus is Spotty restored to those who come after him.

There have been several celebrities in that part of the forest known as "The Broadcast Area" because it was from here that the first broadcast of the lyrebird was made by the Australian Broadcasting Commission, in the early thirties. I can still recall my excitement as I listened, with my ears "glued" to the radio set and scarcely daring to breathe lest I spoil the reception, as the lyrebird's song from Sherbrooke came to me in my suburban home.

Here, in the Broadcast Area, lived "Silvertail" who was renowned for his magnificent long tail and powerful melodious voice which frequently sent me hurrying to his territory, in 1939–40. This bird, however, was much less friendly than his illustrious neighbour, Timothy.

In the early fifties, this area was occupied by "The Wanderer", so named because he exhibited a remarkable capacity for wandering far from home, often being found nearly half a mile from his principal mound. This bird was characterized by his habit of carrying his lyrates crossed and one of them was noticeably less curved than the other. He also had a pigmentation fault, i.e., a large white spot, on his right side. It was always a great pleasure for me to stand beneath his lofty perch on a winter's morning before the dawn and listen to his glorious notes.

I am indebted to this bird for a remarkable record on behaviour. One Sunday evening, just before dusk, The Wanderer was quietly preening before going to roost when, suddenly, he ceased preening and peered intently into the darkening forest below him. Then he uttered a note of annoyance, glided to earth and began a murderous pursuit of a plaintail which had innocently intruded into The Wanderer's territory. Had he managed to catch him, I am sure he would have thrashed him; but the younger bird took refuge in a wombat's burrow. The Wanderer, like a big bully, stood guard at the entrance and strode to and fro, swishing his tail angrily and uttering the most unlyrebird-like notes I have ever heard. His notes were guttural, harsh, croaking . . . he had become a prehistoric creature newly-emerged from the primeval swamp. After a time, the plaintail shot out of the wombat's burrow like a rocket and, springing on to a tall tree-fern, he glided off down the hillside with the baffled Wanderer still cursing loudly in hot pursuit.

It may be appropriate here to interpose a note in answer to a question which is often asked, namely "Do lyrebirds fight?" The behaviour of The Wanderer, just described, suggests that they do — occasionally, at least. Timothy certainly would have punished Bobtail for his impertinence as mentioned on page 96, and Spotty was frequently observed to "corner" a plaintail and hold him at bay, cowering with fear, until

The Wanderer perching during an early morning concert.

The kookaburra (or Laughing Jackass) whose loud call resounds through the forest at break of day is himself a famous Australian. But he is a robber and frequently attacks lyrebirds feeding at ground level or females carrying food to chicks in elevated nests.

something happened to distract the older bird's attention. However, at other times, the birds do actually strike one another, and clusters of feathers found in the forest from time to time are evidence that a brawl has occurred. R. C. Chandler, writing of the lyrebirds in the Bass River Valley over sixty years ago, relates having once seen two male lyrebirds fighting like roosters, using their beaks and sharp claws, and sometimes tripping over their tails! More recently Mr. Richard Brown, of Nunawading, Victoria, informed me that on 31st May, 1965, he had observed a changeling lyrebird make a sudden attack on a plaintail. The latter screamed and struggled, and fell on its back, in which position it was held by the other bird with one claw while he raked feathers out of its breast with the other! The aggressor tried to peck the other bird, and once seized its beak in his. The two birds remained in this position for some time, the plaintail screaming and struggling occasionally, though mostly remaining passive, while the other bird slowly raked its breast. There were several other lyrebirds nearby, but they showed no concern, except when the plaintail screamed. Eventually the changeling released his hold and the other bird escaped, to be chased over logs and under ferns by the changeling, for a further five minutes, after which both birds resumed feeding. Mr. Brown took a number of photographs of the two birds during the fight.

"The Wanderer" was succeeded by another bird known as "The Crescent" because he carried a crescent-shaped pigmentation fault in the broad of his back; his lyrates were also carried in the crossed position.

During the past few years the Broadcast Area was occupied by a bird known simply as "Crossed Lyrates", for obvious reasons. He very closely resembled "The Wanderer", but was much more approachable. He mated with "Droopy" in 1963 and, one day in September when I was visiting the nest and chick, I heard noises from down the gully which indicated that there was another chick down there being fed by his mother. I hurried down . . . to find Crossed Lyrates giving a perfect imitation of his chick and spouse at meal time! He entertained many visitors from overseas and was the star in colour films made by Helmut Bart of Germany, and Harold Pollock of Sydney, in 1964.

I spent many happy hours in the company of this bird, but was dismayed to see him limping badly and carrying a broken wing, in December 1964. His principal mound, which was also Silvertail's favourite mound in 1939, was not used in 1965, but there is now another "friendly" mature male bird in occupation of this territory and, strange to say, he too has crossed lyrates!

There have been other birds of special interest and, among the females, perhaps the one I called "The Friendly Female" was the best known. Actually, I had two such birds so named which lived on opposite slopes of a steep gully in which "Sherbrooke Falls" was once a feature. One day in September 1947, I was returning from a visit to The Friendly Female on the southern side of the gully and, as I was walking through the forest on the northern slope, my eye was attracted to a bright spot like a glistening dew drop, in a clump of sword grass near ground level. It was the eye of a female lyrebird brooding her solitary egg in a very well concealed nest and, as she moved her head, the light was reflected from her eye on to mine. Her chick was hatched a few days later, but

A young admirer tempts Friendly Female with a large worm.

in her first season she was far from friendly. As we became better acquainted over the years, she grew so used to my presence that she just accepted me as part of the environment and used to scratch the earth from under my very boots! As our children grew up they also came to know her, and one of my prized photographic trophies is a picture of one of my young sons playing a game of tug of war with "Friendly", over a large worm. "Friendly" won!

Usually, this bird followed the normal lyrebird time-table, so far as egg-laying and hatching are concerned; but in 1955, her chick (then aged six weeks) did not leave the nest until November 15.

Her 1959 chick became one of the star juniors of Sherbrooke Forest, but he disappeared from my principal study area towards the end of April 1965. I have not seen Friendly herself since 1962 and presume that she is now dead.

"The Photogenic Female", for many years a Sherbrooke personality, poses in striking fashion to display the detail of her wings and tail feathers.

Yet another of Sherbrooke's famous lyrebirds is the female "Droopy", so named on account of her habit of drooping her off-side wing when she becomes aware that she is being observed. She has built a number of nests, sometimes at or near ground level, but on several occasions at heights of fifty to sixty feet. Her admirers have included Spotty and Crossed Lyrates. She is normally quite unobtrusive, though not unfriendly, and it is a most enjoyable experience to find her, during the springtime, industriously scratching for worms among the ferns whilst softly clucking to her new season's chick as he shelters under the ferns nearby or disports himself on a low branch overhead.

Among the celebrities of Sherbrooke is a male blackbird. During the past five years, this bird, which is of course free-flying, has paid me the compliment of visiting me in various parts of the forest and hopping about near my feet. With his bright orange beak and shiny black feathers he is quite striking in appearance. He has developed the habit of singing while he is near me sharing the melody of a lyrebird and, most remarkably, his song at this time is a most charming imitation of the lyrebird itself, delivered in a very soft voice as if he were too modest to compete with the Master of Song himself. He is a frequent visitor at Mrs. McPherson's home ("The Cottage") and also flies to her when she is in the forest.

Although Sherbrooke Forest is the one place where the lyrebird may be seen and the exquisite melody of its voice heard without undue effort, fortunately there are many other places where the bird still thrives.

But there are no grounds for complacency. Every year many birds fall victim to foxes and feral cats, and even to domestic cats which wander from their owner's homes at the margin of the forest.

The friendly blackbird.

This lyrebird was lucky! His tail was bitten off by a fox, but the bird escaped with his life!

Yet the greatest threat lies in the loss of habitat as the needs of a growing population exact their inexorable toll of our virgin bushland.

There was a time when Gippsland was known as the Land of the Lyrebird, but that was long ago, before the axe and the fire-stick had left their marks. For many years there has been a comparative truce, but who knows when the giant "Progress" will march eastward once again?

Those who have witnessed the practical extermination of the mallee fowl cannot ignore the threat to the lyrebird.

Over one hundred years ago John Gould wrote, "Were I requested to suggest an emblem for Australia from amongst its avifauna, I should without the slightest hesitation select the lyrebird as the most appropriate". We of today, in supporting this tribute to one of the most distinguished birds in the world, must recognize it as our duty as well as our privilege to protect the lyrebird so that those for whom we hold it in trust may enjoy a heritage not less wonderful than our own.

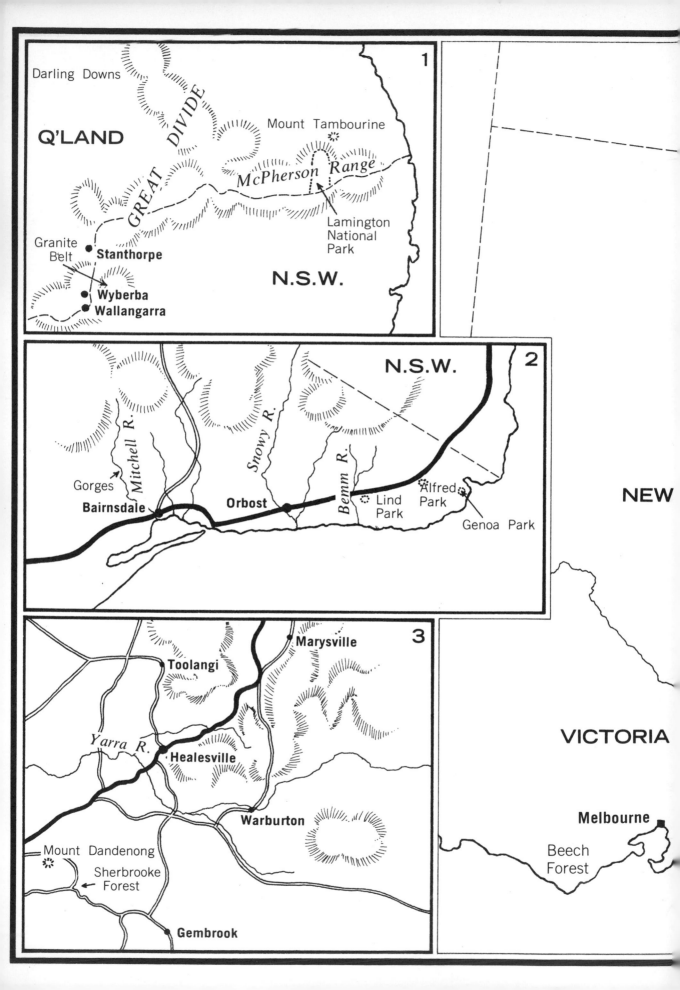

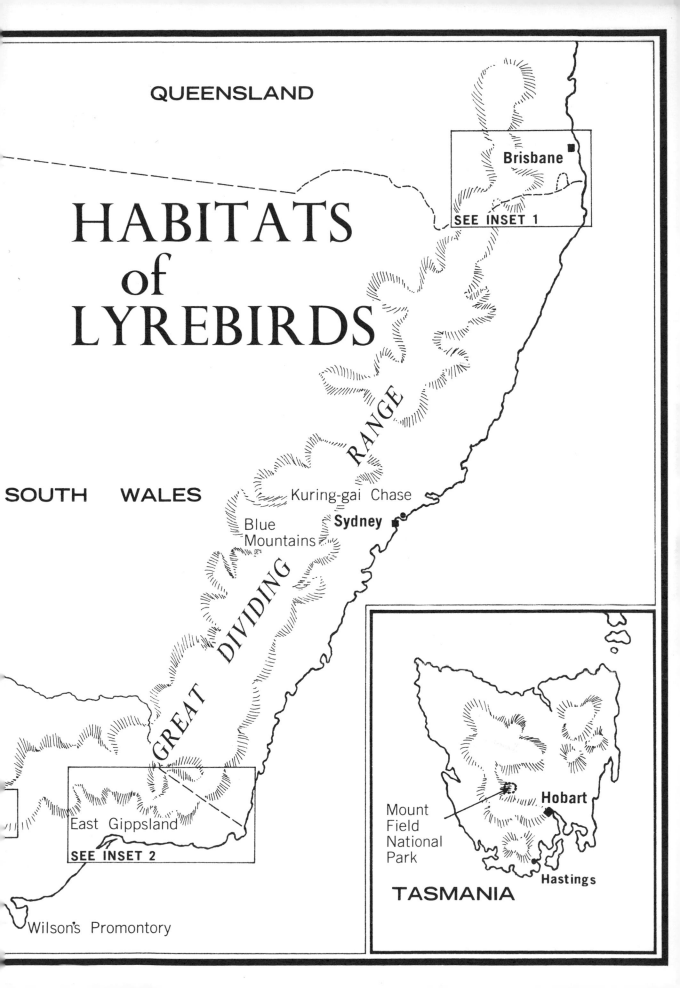

QUEENSLAND

HABITATS
of
LYREBIRDS

SOUTH   WALES

Brisbane

SEE INSET 1

Kuring-gai Chase

Blue
Mountains

Sydney

GREAT DIVIDING RANGE

East Gippsland

SEE INSET 2

Wilson's Promontory

Mount
Field
National
Park

Hobart

Hastings

TASMANIA

BIBLIOGRAPHY

GENERAL

Aflalo, F. G., *A Sketch of the Natural History of Australia*, Macmillan & Co., London; 1896

Becker, Ludwig, "The Nest, Egg and Young of the Lyrebird *(M. superba)*", *Trans. Philos. Inst. Vict.*, pp. 153-54; 1855-56

Beilby, J. W., "On the Lyrebird", *Trans. Philos. Inst. Vict.*, Vol. 2, pp. 12-14; 1857

Campbell, A. J., *Nests and Eggs of Australian Birds*, Vol. 1, Pawson and Brailsford, Sheffield, England; 1900

Chisholm, A. H., *The Romance of the Lyrebird*, Angus and Robertson, Sydney; 1960

Cook, L. C., "The Lyrebirds of Poowong", *Emu*, Vol. 8, pp. 220-1; 1909, ibid, Vol. 15, p. 52; 1915, ibid, Vol. 16, p. 101; 1916

Froggatt, W. W., *Some Useful Australian Birds*, Government Printer, Sydney; 1921

Gould, J., *Handbook to the Birds of Australia*, London; 1865. *(M. superba*, Vol. 1, pp. 298 et seq.; *M. alberti*, Supplement)

Littlejohns, R. T., *Lyrebirds Calling from Australia*, Robertson and Mullens, Melbourne; 1943

Mathews, G. M., *Birds of Australia*, Vol. 7, Witherby & Co., London; 1919

Nicholls, E. Brooke, "A Trip to the Bass Valley", *Vict. Nat.*, Vol. 28, pp. 149-57; 1911

Pratt, A., *The Lore of the Lyrebird*, Robertson and Mullens, Melbourne; 1938

Sharland, M. S., "Photographing the Lyrebird", *Emu*, Vol. 30, p. 88; 1930

Smith, L. H., "The Tail of the Lyrebird", *Walkabout*, Vol. 26, No. 6, pp. 11-15; June 1960

Smith, L. H., "Lyrebird, Australia's Meistersinger", *National Geographic Magazine*, Vol. 107, No. 6, pp. 849-857; 1955

Smith, L. H., "Changes in the Tail Feathers of the Adolescent Lyrebird", *Science*, Vol. 147, No. 3657, pp. 510-513; 1965, ibid, Vol. 149, No. 3683, p. 565

Smith, L. H., "Australia's Lyrebird", The *Illustrated London News*, Vol. 229, (No. 6121) pp. 544-45; 1956

Tregellas, T., "Further Notes on the Lyrebird", *Emu*, Vol. 21, pp. 93-103; 1921

Tregellas, T., "The Truth About Lyrebirds", ibid, Vol. 30, p. 243; 1931

Williams, F. J., "The Habits of the Lyrebird", *Southern Science Record*, Vol. 1, p. 87; 1880-82

LYREBIRDS IN CAPTIVITY

Bartlett, A. D., "Notes on the Habits of the Lyrebird in Captivity", *Proc.* Zool. Soc.,

London, pp. 668-9; 27/1/1867

See also *Proc.* Zool. Soc., London, p. 262; 14/5/1868

Chisholm, A. H., "The Story of 'Joe' and 'Zoe' ", The *Argus*; 28/8/1936

Godfrey, F. P., "The Story of 'Jack' ", *Emu*, Vol. 8, pp. 33-34; 1905.

Grey, J. E., *Proc.* Zool. Soc., London, p. 167; 27/3/1866

THE SONG OF THE LYREBIRD

Fleay, David, "Now is the Concert Time of Lyrebirds", *The Australasian;* 27/6/1942

Halafoff, K. C., "Musical Analysis of the Lyrebird's Song", *Vict. Nat.*, Vol. 75, pp. 169-78; 1959

Halafoff, K. C., "Audiospectrographic Analysis of Lyrebird Song", *Vict. Nat.*, Vol. 80, p. 304; 1964 (See also *Vict. Nat.*, Vol. 80, p. 370; 1964)

Halafoff, K. C., "Some Comments on Bird Music", *Vict. Nat.*, Vol. 82, p. 78; 1965

LYREBIRDS IN TASMANIA

Sharland, M. S., "The Lyrebird in Tasmania", *Emu*, Vol. 44, pp. 64-71; 1944

HYBRIDS

O'Donoghue, J. G., "Notes on the Victorian Lyrebird", *Vict. Nat.*, Vol. 31, pp. 11-20; 1914

Chisholm, A. H., "Bird Hybrids — A Remarkable Problem", *Vict. Nat.*, Vol. 81, p. 227; 1964

Hertzog, K. P., "Lyrebird-Fowl Hybrids", *Vict. Nat.*, Vol. 80, p. 313; 1964 (gives additional references)

Hertzog, K. P., "Lyrebird-Fowl Hybrids", *Vict. Nat.*, Vol. 82, p. 87; 1965